RISE
FINDING YOUR EXECUTIVE VOICE

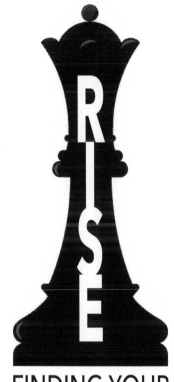

FINDING YOUR EXECUTIVE VOICE

A Story of
Confident Leadership

ANNA CONRAD

IMPACT LEADERSHIP SOLUTIONS
DENVER, COLORADO

First published by
Impact Leadership Solutions
Denver, Colorado

ISBN: 978-1-7336588-0-5

This book is printed on acid-free paper.

Printed in the United States of America

For Madeline. Let your true colors shine through.

TABLE OF CONTENTS

INTRODUCTION

The concept of this book came into existence, like so many other great ideas, while having cocktails. I was celebrating the publication of my first book with a friend, when she innocently asked me why I didn't write about a woman since I have such a strong passion around helping females. My response came out before I had a chance to think about it: because if I wrote a book about a woman, men probably wouldn't read it. However, if I wrote about a man, women would read it.

I hope I am wrong, and people of all genders, races, and employee levels will find this book useful. I have coached and trained thousands of people, and almost every person deals with issues of confidence. Moments of doubt creep into daily activities, sometimes crippling us with inaction, and other times resulting in boisterous, overcompensating behaviors that repels others. The thought "If we can fool others, we can fool ourselves" causes this behavior, but the falsity of this belief is usually lost on us until it is too late and damage has been done.

Although I went to law school to change the world, it is in these last 20 years as an executive coach, facilitator, and speaker that I feel like I make a difference. I have immense gratitude and humility to all of the men and women who have trusted me as their coach and growth partner. Without their honesty, candor, and openness, this book could not have been written or even dreamed of it. It is a weave of the strength and stories of people I have worked with, with my own experience entwined.

THE DILEMMA

CHAPTER 1

Twenty-three. That's how many breaths I've taken so far. And I'm still not calm.

While I'm counting, here's another number: 1551¼. That's how many days I have worked in the same role under the same manager. And about 1371 of these days I've done with my eyes closed. Not literally, of course. That would be career suicide, but that's how well I can do my job.

I'm working on my 41st breath when I hear a tap at my office door. "Come in," I say.

I look up to see Julie peering in, concern on her face. "Are you okay, Mallory?" she asks, closing the door quietly behind her and sitting in the seat across from my desk. "I take it the meeting didn't go well." She must have noticed the quick retreat to my office after the meeting, my eyes glued to the floor.

"You can say that," I reply, mixing defeat with sarcasm. "I'm not sure if I'm mad, embarrassed, or hurt. Actually, I think I'm all of those, as well as confused." I put my head in my hands.

"What happened?" she asks.

"You probably guessed that I didn't get the promotion. But that's not what's upsetting me." I look at her and pause. "That's a lie. I *am* a little upset by that," I admit sheepishly. "But what I'm really upset about is the excuse Dale gave me."

I pause for another couple of seconds to collect myself. After being in my job for a long time as a Director, I'm sure I deserve the promotion to a Senior Director or even a Vice President. I look up at Julie and realize I was also a little angry at her; she's the one who persuaded me to talk to Dale about the promotion. Now I feel like a fool.

"I did everything just as we practiced," I explain. "I showed Dale the spreadsheet I put together with what my team had done and how we helped the department." To emphasize this point, I motion to the spreadsheet on the desk.

"I pointed out that my last three performance reviews were almost perfect scores. There was really no reason for him to say 'no,' but say 'no' he did," I tell her with a wry smile and a sweep of my right hand.

"What reason could he possibly have given you?" Julie asks incredulously.

"Wellllll . . . ," I reply, drawing out the word. "Dale admitted I was really good at my role. He said I had surpassed his expectations in almost every way." I lowered my voice and my eyes. "Then he said that before he could promote me, I need to be seen as a 'true leader.'" I raise my hand in air quotes to emphasize the last two words. "Dale said I need to work on this before I can become a VP. He also said I need to improve my 'executive presence'—whatever that means!" I say with more air quotes as I roll my eyes.

Puzzled, Julie looks at me. "What do you think he meant by that? That sounds like yet another buzz term like 'strategic' and 'world class.'"

I feel my face flush. I think, "I don't know what 'executive presence' means. I only know that I don't have the promotion. And if I don't have 'executive presence,' what am I doing even being a Director?"

Lowering my eyes again, I admit in a soft tone, "I, um, kind of ended the meeting and ran out before I could ask him to clarify. I didn't want him to see me upset. I had a feeling that would add to his bad impression of me."

After Julie leaves, I can't concentrate. Thoughts whirl around me. "Dale was not trying to be hurtful. I know his praise for my work and my team's work is heartfelt. What bothered me the most is Dale's tapping into my fear. He somehow homed in on my belief that I don't *deserve* to be an executive. Now I know others feel the same about me."

I take a gulp of air, swallowing the panic as I realize, "I have been fooling no one."

CHAPTER 2

"**O**kay, I'm done with my pity party. I'm ready to take action," I announce to myself. It would've sounded more courageous if I were talking to my manager instead of my bathroom mirror. But I have to start somewhere.

I turn away from my reflection to join my husband in the kitchen. Greg and I have been married for fourteen years. Although we've gone through a few rough times, he is still the one I turn to when I need to talk. He knows when I need to vent and when I need advice. It wasn't always like that. Early in our marriage, he had an annoying habit of trying to fix everything for me, even when I didn't need help. I have learned to tell him when I need him to just listen and when I need his advice—and he respects that most of the time.

I grab the asparagus Greg had washed and begin snapping the ends. I see him push a strand of his greying hair aside with his forearm, his hands covered with flour. After passionately describing my conversation with Dale, I take a breath. Good naturedly, he points out the asparagus did nothing to deserve my wrath.

I look down into the bowl of splintered asparagus and grimace. I leave it on the counter and throw myself into a chair, reaching for the glass of red wine Greg had poured for me.

My tirade dies down as I sip the wine, but questions linger. "It isn't just that I didn't get the promotion. I'm frustrated by the vagueness of what I'm lacking. What is executive presence? What do I need to do to show I have it?"

"Maybe you should stop wearing sweats to the office," he offers jokingly.

"They're jeans, not sweatpants," I protest, looking down at the jeans I'd worn to work that day. "I get your point. But it isn't only that." I blow out a frustrated breath.

"I don't know what it means to be an executive, other than wearing a suit and going to a lot of meetings. I know that the good executives—and Dale is one of them—have something that makes me want to listen to them. They *make* me want to follow them. I'd really like to be like that," I say softly.

The longing in my tone surprises me. "I just need to find out how."

CHAPTER 3

The following morning as I stand in the breakroom stirring creamer into my coffee, I make a commitment to myself to be an organization archeologist. In this role, I will pay attention to people all day to see if I can identify characteristics that could be described as "executive." As I mindlessly stir my coffee, I wonder whom I'd come across during the day that I'd describe as having executive presence. The answer becomes apparent during the 10 o'clock R&D meeting.

I carefully watch Janette, the R&D Team Lead, as she leads the discussion on potential challenges. Janette has a way of talking with confidence that's both strong and humble. She doesn't think with blinders on.

At one point during the discussion, Janette directs her gaze to John, a quiet man in his mid-thirties. She asks him what he thought the challenges of the new system would be. John, who I'd never heard speak up during a meeting, explains a disconnect in the process with fantastic clarity. I look around the room. Everyone is nodding, and a new respect for John settles over the group.

I realize that Janette has a gift: She states her opinion but doesn't do so with an ego that overwhelms others. She doesn't shut people down or interrupt; she is interested in what people think, even if their views go against hers.

I approach her after the meeting and ask if she would join me for lunch. What's her secret? What makes her so confident? What makes people listen to her? Yes, she knows what she's talking about, but it's *more* than that. And I'm determined to figure out what it is.

CHAPTER 4

Janette and I buy our food and walk past the groups of teams eating together. We found a small table against the wall flanked by fake Cyprus trees.

I smile shyly at Janette as she unwraps her sandwich. "This is going to sound weird, but I have something to ask you," I begin.

She looks up and smiles. "What is it, Mallory? By the way, thank you for inviting me to lunch. I know we've worked together for almost four years, and I think this is the first time we've talked outside of any meeting."

"I know," I respond. "I'm so glad you were free." I don't mention that I probably would've lost my nerve if we scheduled the lunch for a later date.

I took a deep breath and lowered my voice so no one else would hear. "I received feedback from my manager that I need to work on coming across as more of an executive. And I'm not really sure what he means. I know part of it is confidence. That is, I don't project the same level of confidence as he does . . . or as *you* do," I add bashfully.

"I remember when I first met you. I don't know what it is, but you were a lot different. It seems like in the last couple of years you have changed. You've always come across as very capable. But there's something about you now," I look at her, searching for words. "You project a different level of confidence. But it's not the kind of confidence that Roberto used to have," I add sheepishly.

"Remember how he used to walk into a room and people were afraid to say anything? I mean, he never did anything that was really bad; it was just a vibe he gave off—an 'I know my shit, so don't disagree with me' vibe," I say with a laugh.

Janette rolls her eyes in exaggerated animation, "Yeah. I remember. I used to think he was so arrogant, but then he changed. He was actually my inspiration, and I'm so glad you have seen a change in me, too. Most people don't know this, but I've been working hard with an executive coach. She has helped me understand who I want to be and how to get there. It has been difficult, and it means so much to me that you notice. I have a long way to go, but I feel good about the progress I've made," she explains.

I nod. "I invited you to lunch to ask you what your secret is. Now I guess I know."

In fact, I feel relief knowing there's something that can help me, too. I ask, "So, it takes a lot of hard work? But you make it look so easy, Janette."

"Ha!" she replies. "Hard work is an understatement. I'm not trying to change who I am; I'm only trying to make myself a better version of me. If you're interested, I'm happy to share the name of my coach. She has worked with a few other people at our company."

I accept her offer with gratitude, and that afternoon, I approach Dale with a request for hiring a coach. Dale quickly said yes, then tells me he's worked with an executive coach throughout his career.

"If it weren't for my coach, I would still be the supervisor in a call center who upset everyone wondering why I wasn't getting promoted."

CHAPTER 5

"You must be joking," I say to my new coach, shaking my head in astonishment.

The woman sitting across from me smiles in amusement. We've only been talking for a few minutes, but I already feel comfortable with her.

"No," she says, shaking her head. "I will take that as a compliment, though."

I look at Sonia, the executive coach I had agreed to work with. We are sitting at a two-person table tucked in the back of a coffee shop. Sonia's grey eyes shine with amusement as she sips her coffee.

I ask her who else she has worked with at my company. To my surprise, she mentions a former manager of mine, Tom. In exchange for the chance to work on a new product line, I worked for Tom for a short while and ignored everyone's warnings about his domineering management style. But my determination lasted only seven months before I transferred. The experience wasn't worth the misery of dealing with his aggressive behavior.

"I had heard a while ago he was going to be fired," I say to Sonia, shaking my head. "Then all of a sudden, people started to say what a great leader he is. I have two colleagues who work for him now. They swear he's the best manager they've ever had. I don't get it."

Sonia nods as she pushes a lock of blonde hair behind her right ear. "That's so good to hear!" She smiles. "Tom worked hard. I'm really proud of him."

"Well," I grimace, "if you can help Tom, you can help *anyone*. But my problem is the opposite of Tom's." I tilt my head slightly and say, frowning, "I want to work on increasing my confidence, so I can be seen as a strong leader. Tom probably worked on toning down his confidence."

Sonia explains that the first step in the coaching process is to help the coachee figure out *who* he or she wants to be. Then the focus shifts to *how* to achieve that.

"Overall, I like who I am," I respond. "I'm a good person, and I don't want to become someone else."

As I say this, I realize I mean it sincerely. I *am* happy with who I am—as a mother, sister, wife, friend, and manager. I don't *want* to become somebody else. I don't want to turn into a tyrant or become bossy. That's not me, and it's not who I want to be," I continue, making my voice strong.

"I'm worried that this is what's meant by the term 'executive presence' and who I will become through coaching." These words come out before I even realize I'm saying them.

Looking at Sonia in horror, I stammer, "I'm *so* sorry! I didn't mean that."

"That's alright," she assures me. "That is a real concern and one that's legitimate. First, I need to understand who you want to be as a leader. I can easily give you a list of 'thou shalt' and 'thou shalt not' for you to be seen as a good leader. However, you need to define what that means to you."

Then she asks if I'd ever met someone who said all the right things, looked the right way, and dressed well. But when I walked away, I didn't like or trust that person—and I didn't know why.

"Of course! I know this is a cliché, but I just went car shopping. What a miserable experience! I found a car I really wanted. The salesperson asked me the typical questions: 'What will I use it for? How far do I drive? What's important to me about a car?' But I could tell he wasn't really listening to me. His smile seemed forced, and he even pretended to like my six-year-old daughter who was with me. But I could tell her presence was irritating him."

> I don't want to be seen as trying to be someone I am not.

"Did you end up buying the car?" Sonia asks.

"Not from that dealership," I reply. "I went to another one on the other end of town and bought it. This time, I chose the salesperson I wanted to work with. I walked around the showroom and watched all of them. I chose this young man who must've just started. Honestly, I'm not certain why I picked him. I'm sure he wasn't the most knowledgeable person; he actually had to ask another salesperson answers to some of my questions. But I didn't care. I felt I could trust him because if he didn't know the answer, he would ask. He wasn't trying to only tell me what I wanted to hear so I'd buy the car.

"At one point, his manager came out to answer a couple of my questions. When the response to a question was one the manager didn't think I'd like, he wouldn't give me a direct answer. The salesperson and I just looked at each other, and I could tell he was irritated, too. But I bought the car despite that manager.

"I just don't want to be like that. I want to be honest and be *myself*. I don't want to be seen as manipulating." Then I sit back, noticing the emotion edging into my voice.

"I guess what I am getting at is that I don't want to be seen as trying to be someone I'm not. I like being authentic and genuine," I say emphatically.

I lean forward, the slight tilt in my head giving away my sense of uncertainty. "But if I *don't* change, my career is limited. Is it worth it? Is having a career worth being a phony?" Sighing, I admit, "Sonia, I don't know what to do."

I have just named one of my biggest fears that I didn't even know I had. I want to be successful. I want a promotion. But it is more critical for me to be *happy with who I am* and not be a phony.

Sonia took a sip of her coffee, compassion in her eyes. "I don't want you to be someone you're not either, Mallory," Sonia says. "My job isn't to make you into a clone or mold you into the perfect executive. It's to help you be the best person professionally you can be."

Her words sound good but don't make sense to me. After all, isn't the point of my coaching with Sonia to *change*? If I were already perfect, why would I need to work with her?

I tell her about my manager saying I need to be more like an executive, and I share the revelations I had watching Janette, who gave me a context and examples. "Her honesty about how hard she worked to change inspires me," I say.

"Like Janette did, you are entering a new phase in your career," Sonia explains. "The skills that have made you successful so far aren't enough as you move into an executive role. The good news is you've already changed without realizing it. You are a different person now than when you began your career. Chances are, you're already emulating some of the behavior you admire in Janette without realizing it."

She's right. I recall one change in particular after observing Janette. I found myself seeking out Alex's advice on a technical issue. Although Alex has been on my team for over five years, I'd

> The skills that have made me successful so far are not the ones I need to be an executive.

rarely go to him with questions because he's a "heads down" employee. That means he's self-sufficient, never makes a fuss, and gets his work done. He doesn't speak up much or offer suggestions. But after I explained my challenge with the new system, he quickly offered an idea. Brilliant in its simplicity, his solution saved me a lot of time troubleshooting.

Sonia goes on to explain that, during our work together, we'll look at what has made me successful and what it will take for me to progress in my career.

But she gives me a warning. "Our work won't always be comfortable. Most change isn't. I tell my clients they'll know they are growing if they feel uncomfortable. If the person I'm working with tells me something is easy—that the new behaviors or the different way of thinking feels natural—then I know I'm not pushing enough.

"I will provide you with the tools and skills necessary to become the person you want to be, whether it's an executive or a phenomenal individual contributor.

"What this means, though, is that there will be times—a lot of times, actually—that you will feel disingenuous. You'll feel like a phony. It isn't until the behaviors we work on become natural that it will click. In the meantime, your need for authenticity will not be met. You will even feel like a fraud at times.

17

"It's important to remember, though, that you'll be trying new behaviors that aren't natural to you—yet."

I feel my heart quicken. Sonia has just tapped into another one of my biggest secrets, and she hasn't even realized it.

CHAPTER 6

I stare at my office door, my body tense with anticipation. I wait. And I wait. I keep staring expectantly at the door, bracing myself for the security guard to barge into my office with some faceless HR person.

I imagine three people coming in yelling at me to get up. In my daydream, they grab my arm, yank me out of my chair, and throw the photo of my children and other personal belongings into a box. They tell me my scheme has been discovered; they know I am a fraud, and I need to get out.

I suddenly wake up from the daydream, startled by its clarity. I fight to focus on the report lying on my desk.

A variation of this daydream has happened all my professional life. Sometimes the fantasy is more intense than others. But lately, it's been almost paralyzing. At times, the anxiety makes it hard to concentrate. It stops me from speaking up. It renders me nearly paralyzed. It makes my voice crack when I am feeling even the slightest bit uncertain.

My fear of being discovered as incompetent on technical issues had eased as I gained more knowledge. Now I'm sure I know what I'm doing, at least from a technical sense. People come to me for questions about processes and procedures, and even my peers have started to ask.

Proud of my knowledge, I like the status of the being the subject matter expert. It wasn't until my review that I realize I needed to be more than the go-to person for technical information. I need to have people turn to *me* for management and interpersonal issues.

This is when the daydream comes back in full force.

A soft knock on my door is followed by Jose leaning into my office. "Do you have a second?" he asks.

"Of course," I respond, motioning him in.

"You okay?" he asks, looking at me thoughtfully. "You look a little dazed."

"I'm just thinking," I reply. "Quick question: who did you ask for help when you and John were having that issue a couple of months ago? I know you ended up working it out with him, but was there someone you went to for advice?"

His eyebrow raised in a quizzical gesture. "Whyyyy?" he asked, drawing out the last part of the word.

"I just want to know. Don't worry; you aren't in trouble," I assure Jose. "I'm curious about who you and others go to for advice on that kind of stuff."

Jose has been working for me for almost three years, and we have always had an honest relationship. Even so, I could tell he was hesitant to answer my question.

"Well," he begins slowly, "I asked Darlene for advice since she has worked with John for a while. And I know she's had issues with him in the past." He looks up thoughtfully. "I also discussed the issue with Walter. He's always good at helping me with this stuff."

I look at him, hoping my features reflect the openness I was trying to convey.

"Can I ask you something else?"

"Sure."

"I'm just curious. Why don't you ever come to me with questions about these things?" He looks startled. "You and I have always had a good relationship, but—" he hesitates, "I don't know how to say this without hurting your feelings."

"Go on," I encourage him. "I really want to know."

"Well," he pauses, looking apologetically at me. "You are really good with the stuff we do here. It's just I don't think you are comfortable with conflict. And most of the problems I've been having are because people aren't doing their jobs. I think if I come to you with these issues, you would volunteer to do the work yourself, so we wouldn't be upset with each other."

Still feeling apprehensive, he continues, "But I honestly think that certain things I deal with need to be handled more forcefully. And I know you aren't comfortable with that."

The truthfulness of his words envelops me. *He is right. I do not like conflict, and I will do almost anything to avoid it.* But I had always seen my peacekeeping skills as a strength, especially compared to my colleagues' who are like bulls in a china shop.

"Don't get me wrong," he quickly adds. "You are great to talk to. I always feel better because you are such a good listener. But sometimes I need advice. Please don't be upset. You asked me to tell you the truth."

I thought about the days when my office seems to have a revolving door with people coming to me with their problems. People know I am always there to listen.

As Jose finishes talking, I realize that people only come to vent. They don't ask me for advice. And to be honest, I never offer it. I don't think it is up to me tell people how they should do things. After all, I don't know what is best for people, and who am I to give advice? I need help a lot myself.

At least this is what I thought until I started working with Sonia.

CHAPTER 7

The following Monday, I arrive at the coffee shop for my session with Sonia. I hurry in, noticing Sonia in the back with two steaming cups in front of her.

"Confidence." I proclaim as I greet her while setting my tote on the floor and settling into my seat.

She raises an eyebrow.

"This is what I want to work on," I explain. I felt like a little girl again, telling Santa what I wanted for Christmas.

I look at her hopefully, a hesitant smile on my lips.

"What do you mean by confidence?" she asks, openly interested. "What does that mean to you?"

I explain what I regard as confidence, thinking about Janette as I describe it. "It's people noticing you when you walk into a room. It's people listening when you talk. It's having your direct reports not second-guess you. It's your peers acknowledging your ideas. It's believing I am good enough, and having my kids do what you tell them to."

She laughs at the last part. "I'm not sure if I can help with that! I have a teenager, and I know how impossible that can be."

"How about the rest?" I ask, my hand wrapping around the warm mug.

"I'm afraid I can't teach you confidence," she says with the corners of her mouth pointing down in a frown.

My lighthearted mood and determination take a dive. "But this is what I really need to work on." My voice sounds almost pleading. "I honestly think this is at the core of everything I need to fix about myself."

Sonia's eyes reflect sympathy and understanding as she says, "I know it seems like that, but confidence isn't something you learn, like riding a bike. *It isn't an actual skill.* It's a feeling you have in yourself and in others.

"I can't teach you how to be confident, but I can give you tools to feel confident about who you are and, in turn, to have others feel confident about you."

> Confidence isn't a skill. It's a feeling you have in yourself and in others.

I sit back in my chair, letting her words find meaning.

Thinking about Janette, I realize Sonia is correct. Janette's actions aren't what make her confident; the person she portrays herself to be is confident. She doesn't have to yell to have people listen to her. Some people talk over others, but just because their voices are loud doesn't mean they have confidence in what they're saying.

I nod slowly. I'd hoped to walk out of the session with all the skills needed to project confidence. I even have my imaginary superhero cape ready.

I'll just have to keep that cape ready for another day.

CHAPTER 8

"I'll let you in on a secret," Sonia says, leaning closer to me. Her eyes twinkle, and I feel mine respond in anticipation.

"A confident person doesn't insist that everything goes his or her way. I have been doing this a long time, and there's one thing I know for certain: *It's usually not the loudest person in the room who is the most confident.* Typically, the loudest person is trying to prove something to himself or herself. They are covering up insecurities they're sure others can see.

"True confidence is not insisting on getting a certain result," she continues. "It's knowing you can handle *anything* that comes your way."

Sonia asks me to think about a successful project I'd been a part of, even if I wasn't the lead. I mention the rollout of Dranger, the new software that changed a major business line.

"As you did the rollout, did any deadlines or processes change?" she asks.

I laugh. "Only about every two hours."

"But did you still believe it would be successful?" she asks.

"Without a doubt. The changes always made sense."

"Did the leader seem phased by the changes? Did he seem stressed?"

"No, he wasn't worried," I answer.

"Ahh. So, he was able to go with the changes others suggested?"

"Absolutely! He welcomed everyone's input, but he had the final say," I explain.

Sonia smiles broadly. "Believe it or not, it takes a lot of confidence to listen to others and make decisions, even if the decisions will be unpopular. Confident people don't insist that *their* way is the only way. Being confident means they're open to others' ideas and opinions. They aren't afraid to be wrong. "This isn't easy," she quickly adds.

"Most people feel a strong sense of responsibility for projects and teams they're responsible for. This stress often leads people to manage with a heavy hand, wanting and needing a say in most decisions and actions. While the intention is good—they want the team and project to succeed—the behavior lends itself to lack of engagement and innovation from the staff."

> Confidence is knowing you can handle anything that comes your way

To illustrate this, Sonia tells me the story of her CEO client, Kyle, who heads a $600 million company. The company had a reputation for being a terrible place to work. When Kyle received a 360 feedback assessment, it included harsh criticisms about his leadership style. After an initial week of seething in anger, Kyle called Sonia. He had spent the past week blaming the respondents. He told Sonia he began the week thinking they all needed to grow up and realize it was *just business*. They shouldn't take his personality so personally. After all, he (not them) was the CEO.

His attitude changed the following Thursday when he offered to help his teenage daughter with her homework. The daughter was sitting at the dining room table concentrating hard on a math problem. She was biting her bottom lip, a habit she'd had since being a toddler.

"What are you working on?" Kyle asked his daughter.

Her head jerked upward, breaking her concentration. "I'm trying to figure out this math problem on complex numbers."

"Can I help?" he offered, leaning over her shoulder.

"Uh, no thanks, Dad, I'll figure it out," she assured him.

"Okay. Let me know if you change your mind," and he left the room.

Later that evening, his wife Terri was helping their daughter. He approached the duo, offering his help again. His daughter, looking less bleak than when he saw her earlier, said, "No thanks, Dad. Mom's helping me. We've got it." His wife looked at him apologetically but quickly turned back to their daughter and the math problem. He left the room feeling excluded.

As he and his wife were getting ready for bed, Kyle expressed his hurt feelings. She nodded in understanding. "I know you want to help, but remember what happened the last few times you tried to help her with her homework? She ended up crying."

He responded, "I don't know why she cried. I was just showing her how to do the problems. She shouldn't be so sensitive. That won't get her anywhere in life." He told me the shock he felt at his own obtuse reply. In that instant, he realized he had been saying the same thing about the 360 respondents.

It's one thing to have people at work not like you; it's another when it involves your own daughter.

Over the weekend, he paid close attention to his behavior to his children and his wife. He watched their reactions to what he said, and he noticed the difference between his relationship with them and how they related with his wife. A startling realization hit. *He behaved the same way to his family as he did at work: blunt, unapologetic, and with little compassion.* He realized he didn't want to be that person at home or at work. He didn't want someone to do what he said only because his name was on the company's letterhead. Instead, he wanted people to respect him for his knowledge and his leadership skills, not because they were afraid to lose their job or their allowance.

During the next all-hands meeting, he insisted people attend in person or watch live on the company's intranet. Kyle stood in front of everyone and apologized for his past behavior. He thanked people for giving him the feedback on his 360, and he admitted he was humbled by the comments. He said he planned to work on becoming a better leader and a better man—both at work and at home.

"I can tell you," Sonia comments, "the company made a massive switch at that moment. The humility Kyle conveyed showed everyone that it's okay to be open, that perfection isn't expected. There have been many changes since then, including a drastic reduction in voluntary turnover and a higher level of employee engagement.

"No one looks at Kyle as being less confident. If anything, it is the opposite," she adds. "It takes confidence to be vulnerable. You have to be confident you can handle the feedback and change your behavior.

"It was when Kyle *wasn't* confident—when he was afraid of losing control as a CEO and a father—that he appeared weak to others. It doesn't take much strength to pound your fist on the table. But it does take strength to be open to change. True confidence is not thinking you'll get a great result; it's knowing that you can handle any result.

"I have worked with hundreds of leaders of all levels, and the truly confident ones are not those shouting the loudest. The most confident ones don't need the spotlight. It's actually the opposite."

Sonia goes on to say that confident leaders aren't afraid to be wrong and listen more than they speak. They don't seek attention or others' approval, and they don't pass judgment. Indeed, they celebrate other people's success.

"Confident leaders know that just because someone else is successful doesn't mean that they are not. Their happiness and approval come from within, which is why they can take risks.

"And although they are competitive, they seek small victories. To them, the small victories are more important than the larger ones. Because of this, truly confident people can be innovative and change. They aren't tied to the outcome because they know they can handle whatever comes their way.

"That's why they're good at introducing people to one another. They aren't afraid of sharing resources or knowledge. They know that whatever good comes from people connecting will help them as well as others. Mallory, does this make sense?" she asks, her head tilting in inquiry.

I admit that it's a different way to look at confidence. I always thought being confident meant charging forward and not caring what people think. But Sonia is saying the opposite. She says that confidence isn't wearing blinders; it's being humble and not always being the one with the answers.

I nod in agreement, but I still don't completely buy this definition.

CHAPTER 9

The following week while in a project update meeting, I'm listening to the project manager Anika explain that we were behind on the rollout of our new product line. Her calm, assured tone prevents the alarm we'd usually feel due to a revised timeline.

Levi, the senior engineer, interrupts her and claims he will make up the time lost by the delays in the project. "I'm always done ahead of schedule, and this project will be no exception," he states firmly. He's glancing at the project sponsor sitting at the end of the table, hoping for a nod of approval. Despite his assurances, though, I don't believe what Levi says. Based on the fact that he received no nods of approval, I doubt others believe him, either.

As I drive to my coaching session the next morning, I think a lot about that meeting. At the beginning, I relay the events of the meeting to Sonia—and my lack of belief in Levi's ability to execute.

"What you observed is the difference between healthy confidence and too much confidence," she says.

"Too much confidence often causes uncertainty in others. When people are overly confident, they have a win-at-all-cost mentality. This may invoke a threat response in others, causing them to either argue or shut down. Just as harmful, this mindset usually prohibits the person from being open to change and flexibility, both of which are critical in today's business world.

"Overconfident people may fool themselves and others in the short term. This deceit sometimes works. It makes people believe they can do more than they are able to. Overconfidence can lead to people who become prone to risk, and risky behavior can lead to dire consequences," Sonia explains. Then she asks, "Do you remember the reason I gave you about why I couldn't teach you confidence?"

> Overconfidence can lead to risky behavior.

"Of course," I reply. "You said that confidence is a feeling, not a skill. I thought you were crazy when you said that, I admit. But it makes sense now."

"What were you picking up on with Levi? Why do you not believe his team will perform the way he claimed?"

"I don't know," I shake my head. "I know he does good work, but he's also a lot of talk. Most of us roll our eyes when he starts going on and on about how amazing he is and all the projects he's worked on."

Sonia suggests, "So, the lack of confidence may not be what he feels in himself, but the confidence you have in him to keep his word. He may feel confident in his getting the work done, but you aren't confident in his abilities to do so."

I nod slowly as the proverbial light bulb goes off. *Just because Levi claims to have confidence he could get things done doesn't mean I will automatically be confident in his ability to execute.*

Sonia removes a sheet of paper from her briefcase and draws a triangle, which she divided with three lines. She turns the paper toward me so I can see the pyramid.

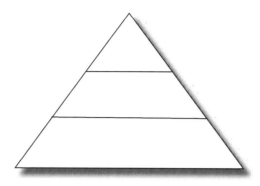

"This is a model that shows the key elements of confidence my team developed. It doesn't matter what country we live in or what level a person has achieved in an organization. We have found that, for someone to be seen as confident, each of these layers must be completed."

With her pen, she points to the bottom of the triangle.

"As we talked about during our first meeting, to have others see you as confident, you must first feel confident in yourself," she says. "The foundation of confidence is who you are on the inside. Only then will others believe in you."

She then writes the words **Confidence in myself** in the bottom row of the triangle.

Then on the level directly above, she writes, **Hear me.**

She turns the paper again to face me and explains that voice and words need to convey the confidence we feel on the inside.

"If you try to sound confident without feeling it, your voice and body language will give you away. There was a study published in the 1960s about the three elements of communication: tone, words, and body language. Although there has been controversy about the validity of the study, I have found the key principal pretty accurate. The study, and my experience, shows that actual words are not as important as the tone of voice you use when saying them. And your body language, is even more impactful than the tone of voice."

"We will discuss this in more depth later," she promises.

I agree, as I feel my excitement build. Now, I think, we're getting to something. I want something tangible to work with. I like action items and processes; I'm not as comfortable with feelings. They're too subjective to do anything with.

Leaning forward, I see what she wrote in the third level of the triangle: **See me.**

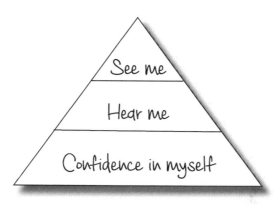

She explains that this level of the Confidence Model refers not only to body language but also to our actions and inactions.

"Think about Levi," she refers to our earlier discussion. "He probably felt confident on the inside—too confident, perhaps. He also sounded confident with the words he spoke in the tone of voice he used. But because he has a history of not performing, which falls into this category, you may not have confidence in his ability."

I nod, understanding the double complexity of this level. It's not only about looking the part, but it is also the actions we show others.

"As Carl W. Buehner and, later, Maya Angelou insightfully proclaimed, people don't remember what you say; they remember how you make them feel," she says.

"It is only when you feel confident on the inside, and exhibit behaviors on the outside, that others will follow you. Being the confident leader others will follow, whether it's over a battle-field or onto the next project. But for this to happen, the rest of the pyramid must be in place."

She points to the top of the pyramid and explains that, too often, new leaders try to start by demanding others follow them, without showing others why they should have confidence in them. "They come into an organization or onto a team and demand changes without first establishing why people should have confidence in them. They may beat their chest and brag about their previous accomplishments, but this is only part of what the team needs to feel confident about. For team members to perform at their best, they must feel confident they can trust the new leader to do what's best for the team, to look out for them and help them be successful.

"Because of this, people may not be engaged and may not perform the work at the level that's needed to be successful. When this happens, they often fail, and ultimately lose confidence in themselves.

"So, you end up with a manager whose team doesn't perform. Eventually, this erodes the confidence she had in herself and negates any confidence the team might have had in her. That's why it's important to take the time to start with the bottom level and build up from there. Otherwise, failure is inevitable."

I pull the paper in front of me and examine it. I have asked Sonia to do precisely as she just said: I wanted tactical advice on what I can do to appear more confident to others. I have watched TED talks, listened to podcasts, and read a dozen articles on the internet looking for a magic bullet. I want a list of things to do and not do. I want to tackle the middle and top of the pyramid. That would be a lot easier than starting at the bottom where she insists we begin.

"What do you think gets in the way of you conquering the first level?" Sonia asks, pointing to "Confidence in myself."

Dozens of thoughts flash through my mind as I ponder the question. I see myself sitting alone at the lunch table my first day of middle school. I hear my college advisor asking me if I was sure I didn't want a teaching certificate instead of a finance degree. And, of course, I remember the humiliation I felt when my manager recently told me I had no "executive presence."

I shift uncomfortably in the café chair. I like Sonia, but I'm not ready to share my thoughts. "I don't know," I lie, hesitation giving away my dishonesty. She looks at me compassionately and pulls out her calendar.

"This will give you something to think about before our next session."

I retrieve my calendar from my tote. "I can't wait," I say with irony, and we schedule our next session.

PART 1
CONFIDENCE IN MYSELF

CHAPTER 10

"It's me!" I say as a greeting when Sonia and I sit down for our next session. The hum of conversation softens the finality of my words.

I settle into my chair, letting the aroma of the coffee surround me with comfort. Sonia looks at me, her brow furrowed in confusion.

I explain that it's my own fault that I am not strong with the bottom of triangle, Confidence in Myself. "I had spent the week trying to understand where my lack of confidence comes from. At first, I blamed others in my past for my self-doubt: harsh teachers, critical parents, lack of support from managers. After thinking about this longer, I realized the stories and memories I had about each person had one thing in common: I believed the words that were said. And I let these words have a more significant impact on my self-worth than others who told me the opposite, people who encouraged me and told me I did okay. I probably made the negative words into something they weren't, morphing them into criticism to fit the perception I had of myself."

"Ah," she nods slightly. "Mallory, you have met your Inner Critic."

"My what?" I ask.

"Your Inner Critic. The voice you hear that tells you when you are doing something wrong, the one who criticizes you," she says, adding, "I call my Inner Critic 'Marge.' I'm not sure why; it was the name that popped into my head when I first noticed her presence.

"Anyway, Marge used to tell me I was going to fail, or if I did something, it wasn't good enough. It's hard to feel confident when you hear this message constantly."

I am surprised. Sonia doesn't seem like someone who would have an Inner Critic.

She notices my look of disbelief and says, "Oh, yes. Marge was my constant companion. I have dealt with a lot of the same things as you. That's why I know what works.

"What I noticed was that Marge was harsher and meaner when the issue was tied to social rejection, like if I was giving a presentation or going to a party where I wouldn't know anyone." Sonia tells me about a study showing that, as far as the brain is concerned, physical pain and intense experiences of social rejection hurt in the same way—that is, the same parts of the brain are triggered.

"So, emotions really do cause pain?" I ask incredulously.

"Absolutely," she confirms. "And remember, 200,000 years of evolution has resulted in instincts that make us fight, flee, or freeze in response to danger, even if the danger is a bad performance review and not a saber tooth tiger chasing us."

Sonia explains that the physiological changes occurring during the fight or flight response are activated to give the body increased strength and speed in anticipation of battling or running. "This is fine for fighting or running away, but it's not great when trying to have a conversation or give a presentation."

Now I understand why I can feel my heart beat faster just thinking about speaking at next month's Board of Directors meeting. I know the Directors won't throw a chair at me or hurt me physically, but the fear I feel is just as intense as if they'd be waiting with a bow and arrow to shoot me as I walk in the door. Both scenarios make me want to run.

I feel the sudden flush of my cheeks coloring my pale skin when I feel nervous. Sonia notices my flushed face, which makes the redness spread even more.

"I know, I look like a lobster," I say, rolling my eyes like my teenage daughter. "It always happens to me when I'm nervous, embarrassed, or anxious. The horrible thing is that blushing embarrasses me, which causes me more anxiety. Of course, this makes me blush even more!"

Sonia explains that blushing is part of the sympathetic nervous system, the network of nerves responsible for triggering my fight or flight reflex. In addition, the response gives me more energy by increasing my blood flow,

> Physical pain and social rejection trigger the same parts of the brain.

sweating to cool me down in a fight, and dilating my pupils to help me see faster. The response also includes vasodilation—the vessels in my face opening to allow the blood to flow more smoothly. It then flows into my face at a faster rate than usual, causing the blushing.

Sonia shakes her head empathetically. "The worst part for people who blush a lot isn't the blushing itself. It's the fact that being terrified of blushing actually causes it. It's a vicious cycle, and yet another way your Inner Critic—your own Marge— grows bigger.

"In fact, your Inner Critic is more detrimental to you than any perceived harm. The stories you tell yourself, and the truth that you are convincing yourself of, causes incredible long-term harm. Convincing yourself you will be hurt *mentally* has lasting effects. We talked before about how your brain doesn't know the difference if the pain is mental or physical. The worst part is that we're the ones causing ourselves this pain."

Sonia pauses to let me process this information.

She's right, of course. I know that I get terrified and freeze, and I tell myself since I'm freezing, I must really be inept. My husband calls this "getting in my own head." It happens quite a bit while learning to ski. I'd be at the top of a run and look down. The slope that appeared flat from the chairlift suddenly becomes deathly steep. He'd tell me to "just point your skis down the hill and go" like it was natural. In those moments of sheer terror, I would have done anything else but that. I'd even take off my skis and carry them down the slope.

"We create fear that causes fight or flight by the stories we tell ourselves," she says to reassure me. "These stories are usually not true, but in the moment, they feel one hundred percent true."

"Yes. Like the story I tell myself that Board members will think I'm incompetent and want me fired," I say. "Afterwards, I think of how foolish that is, but in that moment, I would have bet you a thousand dollars it was true."

"Exactly! Now, the trick is how to recognize those thoughts before they render you powerless or make you want to fight and become defensive," she adds.

I lean forward, eager to hear the secret from her. These thoughts have gotten in my way my whole life, even during the third-grade spelling bee when I couldn't remember how to spell 'scissors,' yet I'd practiced it that morning.

She takes a sip of her tea, raising her eyebrows mischievously.

"How to identify and conquer these thoughts—," she pauses slightly. "We'll get to it at our next session. I have a feeling you will have your hands full with discovery between now and then." She smiles again.

I groan and throw myself dramatically back into my chair. "Janette warned me that coaching would be hard. I thought it would just be the new behaviors; I didn't know it would be frustrating getting the information," I comment, resigned to the idea of waiting.

Sonia softly laughs and says, "We could watch a hundred videos of people who you think of as confident. But this wouldn't do us much good. We need to work on the foundation of the behaviors, the things on the inside that make you *feel* confident. Otherwise, the behaviors won't make you look or feel confident; they will just be awkward."

Looking at her skeptically, I nod. Yet, I still don't fully understand the truth of her words.

CHAPTER 11

Two days later, I'm sipping water from my glass as I look around the conference room. It's late in the afternoon, and my final meeting of the day is in full swing.

I sit among seven other Directors and a few Managers to discuss the status of the rollout of a new line of business. Being selected for the project is an honor, and I feel privileged for having this opportunity. At least that's how I thought at the beginning. Now, four months into it and six months away from the targeted completion, those feelings have shifted.

Clearing his throat, one of the team members, Theo, speaks. He glances nervously around and explains how the latest setback his team faced would affect the project. "They are working overtime, but the vendor we are using keeps pushing out the dates," he explains, running his fingers through his sandy blond hair.

Accusations darken Amanda's olive features. "Theo, the last time we used this vendor, the same thing happened. I don't understand why you didn't find someone else. There is no way my team can finish without that deliverable." She throws down her pen in frustration.

I have worked with the same vendor in the past, and I understood Theo's dilemma. They provide amazing work. The hard part, as he's experiencing, is getting them to stick to deadlines.

For a brief second, I think about mentioning what I did to keep the vendor on schedule. "No," quickly changing my mind, "I don't know Theo's team or what he is asking the vendor to help with. My comments probably won't help him at all, and I'll just sound like a know-it-all," I rationalize. As I think will happen, the topic quickly shifts.

After, while walking to the elevator, I hear a male voice call to me. "Hey, Mallory. Wait up."

It's Theo. He quickens his pace to catch up to me.

"Hi," I say, smiling slightly. "Tough meeting, huh?"

"Tough month," he grunts in agreement. "Listen, I know you have worked with this vendor before, and you got great results. What was your secret? I don't have time to start from scratch with a new vendor. And I know these people offer what we need, but I don't know how to make them stick to the schedule."

"Do you have a few minutes now?" I ask. He nods and motions toward the leather chairs off to the side. We sit down across from each other, and for the next five minutes, I tell Theo what I learned about working with this vendor. At the end of the conversation, he shakes my hand, relief lessening the tenseness around his eyes. He thanks me as he walks me to the elevator.

But going back to my office, I feel guilty for not coming to Theo's aid during the meeting. Even though I knew Amanda was wrong and this vendor was the right choice for the work, I let Theo take the brunt of her anger. I should have told the team I would work with Theo to figure a better relationship. Then I realize I've been listening to my own Marge. And this time it had cost Theo more than it had cost me.

CHAPTER 12

Rain pounds the roof of my car. I drive slowly through the tree-lined streets of the historic district toward the coffee shop for my next session with Sonia. I'm thinking about the incident with Theo and numerous other times I've heard my Inner Critic the past week.

As my awareness of this Inner Critic grows, so does my realization of its effect on my actions—and inactions.

I park the car and walk briskly toward the coffee shop. Shaking the rain off my umbrella, I enter, inhaling the warm, welcoming smell of brewing coffee.

I spot Sonia in the back of the coffee shop. "Is this table reserved for you every day?" I ask jokingly after we say hello.

Laughing, she replies, "No, but it feels that way sometimes. Most of us here are regulars, and we tend to sit at the same tables each time. If this table is taken, I try to avoid the ones I know others prefer. People are creatures of habit, after all."

"Actually, that's one of the things I wanted to talk about today," I say, happy for the easy segue. Sonia listens intently as I tell her about the numerous times I caught my Inner Critic whispering into my ear. "I haven't gone so far as to give it a name but I sure felt its presence.

"It's bizarre," I continue. "Sometimes I feel confident in my knowledge and even bullish about my abilities. But most of the time, I have gnawing self-doubt, which makes me second-guess myself."

"Even the most successful people have moments of doubt," she assures me. "It's natural and even important to your growth. It opens you up for improvement and change. The key is to use these doubts as *humility*, not insecurity. Humility allows you to learn and grow. But when the doubts are based on insecurity, it causes you to feel threatened. And it's this feeling of being threatened that creates defensiveness and the fight or flight response we talked about earlier."

Sonia takes a breath and expounds, "Humility is rooted in strength and openness. It allows you to be vulnerable to growth and change. Lack of confidence is more about insecurity and self-preservation, and this, as we talked about before, often leads to fighting, fleeing, or freezing."

> Humility is rooted in strength and openness. Lack of confidence is rooted in insecurity and self-preservation.

Sonia explains a term coined by psychologist Pauline Clance in 1985 called the Imposter Syndrome. People with the Impostor Syndrome see all the signs of their success, but they feel the reason for it is luck, not hard work, merit, or talent. They live in constant fear that someone will realize they don't deserve to hold their position. Because of this, they look outside of themselves for proof of their success.

I feel heat rise to my cheeks as I recognize myself in her description. My husband recently posted on his Facebook page about an award I had won from a community group. Although he did it because he was proud of me, I got angry at him, embarrassed about the attention it might bring.

My prediction came true two days later. I was in the cereal aisle at the grocery store when I heard a familiar voice—Angie, a neighbor I hadn't seen in a while.

I recall seeing Angie smile widely as she approached me, her two young children trailing behind her. She told me how happy she was I had won the award. "You have done so much for the community. Thanks to you, we were finally able to finish the playground. I was so happy to see your name when the nominations came out. I was even happier to see you won it."

I had smiled at her abashedly, quickly shying from her compliment. "Thank you. But I was fortunate there weren't many nominees this year."

"And that daughter of yours!" she continued while gesturing toward her children. "The kids and I love to watch the videos your husband posts of her soccer games. She is amazing!"

"I agree!" I said appreciatively. "She works so hard, and she has finally seen it pay off this year. It is a tough season, but she's doing great. She's hoping to get a scholarship and play in college."

In the moment, Sonia's explanation of the Imposter Syndrome makes me realize what I had done during this conversation. I had brushed off the compliment about my award and attributed it to luck. But my daughter's accomplishments I embraced fully, crediting her with hard work and skill.

I relay this epiphany to Sonia.

Sonia tells me the majority of her clients have similar feelings. Most of them are high achievers. Because they push themselves constantly, they're often in a stage of growth and discomfort—a perfect breeding ground for Imposter Syndrome feelings.

"This is why I like to call it the Imposter *Experience*, not the Imposter Syndrome. It's actually something you experience, not who you are all of the time."

"Is this a female thing?" I ask, thinking about some men who don't seem to have a problem with confidence. If anything, it's the opposite.

"Actually, no," Sonia replies. "I can honestly say that the Imposter Experience does not discriminate. What I have noticed, though, is that women are more comfortable expressing their insecurity and unease than men. "If anything, working through it is harder for men because these feelings are often regarded as weak. It may not be popular to say this, but in our society, men aren't allowed to be weak—like a lot of women are raised not to be too strong but nurturing instead."

She continues, "Times are changing, and our views of the roles of men and women are slowly morphing, but these stereotypes still exist inside a corporate culture and out. The famous Heidi/Howard experiment is replicated daily. Are you familiar with the study, Mallory?"

I told her I hadn't, so she describes the Harvard study in which professors asked students to read a case based on Heidi Roizen, a well-known venture capitalist in Silicon Valley. They assigned half of the students to read the story of Heidi, and the other half to read a version of the case where the name had been changed to Howard. Students rated Heidi and Howard as equally competent, which made sense since their accomplishments were identical. But they regarded Howard as a more appealing colleague while seeing Heidi as selfish and "not the type of person you'd want to hire or work for."

As Sonia leans back in her chair, her voice softens with concern and sadness. "Most of the women I coach are uncertain how to deal with this paradox. They believe they have to be either competent or liked. They don't think they can be both."

I nod in agreement. "I've been told I'm too nice to be a manager. I can't help it, though. I was taught by my parents that kindness is the most important thing in life. I worry that I will hurt people's feelings," I admit.

"The problem is that this has made it really hard to give negative feedback. So, I often take on more of the work and make excuses for my direct reports when they mess up. I'd rather throw myself under the bus than have others mad at me, even if they are the ones who messed up," I add.

As I say this, I glance up at Sonia who appears to understand. I continue, "I want to be able to give feedback. I know they need it. But every time I start to say something negative, I'm afraid I will hurt their feelings.

"This makes me feel even more like I am failing at my job as a manager," I groan in frustration. "Then I'm even more reluctant to give negative feedback. It's a vicious cycle." I shake my head.

Sonia asks, "Can you see the assumptions you are making about giving negative feedback?"

I shift my weight in my chair uncomfortably.

"Not really," I admit.

"Hmmm. Well, think about this. What are you assuming will happen if you give negative feedback?"

Before I realize what I'm saying, I blurt out, *"That the person won't like me."*

I blush, realizing how juvenile that sounded. Am I really so desperate to be liked?

Sonia doesn't acknowledge my physical response. Instead, she asks if I know that this is 100 percent true—that people will *not* like me if I give them negative feedback.

After a few seconds, I say, "No. They may not like what I tell them, but I don't think they'll hate me for it. Most of my employees ask me what they can do better." Then I chuckle, adding, "Of course, some people don't really want the feedback. I've noticed they just want me to tell them they're doing a good job."

"What about the others? Those who really want to know?"

"Most of my folks want to learn and grow. When they ask for feedback, I give them one or two things. They usually have to ask me, though. I don't want them to feel like they are doing a bad job, and I don't feel comfortable giving them feedback unless they ask," I respond. "Even then, I don't like it. I feel bad criticizing them."

Sonia points to my brown leather notebook and instructs me to turn to a blank page. I reach for the notebook, accidentally brushing against my coffee cup. Steadying the cup with my left hand so it doesn't tip over, I grab the journal and a pen with my right. "That was close," I say.

"The table is a little small," Sonia acknowledges. "Still, I like meeting in coffee shops for coaching sessions. I have discovered that people are a lot more open and focused when we meet away from the office. The casual environment is great for learning, but it has its drawbacks."

"Like the small tables," I finish the thought for her.

"You got it! But it's still better than sitting in a conference room."

She leans back again, her voice returning to a serious tone. She explains the term "mental models" that are stories and assumptions we tell ourselves. They drive our behavior. "I want you to think about this a little more. Specifically, think about the stories and assumptions you tell yourself about giving someone feedback."

On the blank page in my notebook, she tells me to write about a recent situation when I didn't give a direct report needed feedback. I immediately think of Jessica, my newly hired analyst. Last week, Jessica had given me a report that had numerous errors. I had to stay until nine o'clock that night to correct everything so it would be ready for the morning meeting.

Then Sonia instructs me to write down the mental models I have about giving Jessica feedback. My brow furrows in concentration as I write.

Jessica won't like me.

I will hurt her feelings.

I don't know what I'm talking about.

It is my fault she got it wrong.

It is my responsibility to fix it.

Jessica knows more than I do.

It is easier to fix it myself.

Jessica will quit.

She will tell everyone, and they won't want to work with me.

She will go to HR.

HR will think I am a terrible manager.

I look up from my notebook and roll my shoulders to stretch the muscles.

"Look at what you wrote," Sonia says. "If these are the stories you're telling yourself, no wonder you hesitate to speak up. Most people would be afraid to give feedback if these thoughts were going on in their heads, too."

I smile weakly, grateful for her understanding.

"So, let's take an honest look at these thoughts because they're getting in your way of being confident enough to give feedback in the moment." Sonia's tone is all business, and it gave me confidence to look at what I wrote.

Mental models drive my behavior.

Sonia tells me to reread each mental model and cross out any items that aren't 100 percent true.

I evaluate each one, trying hard to remove any emotions while doing it. My inner strength rises with each item I cross off. By the time I finish, I've crossed off every item. A sense of relief replaces my feelings of trepidation. *I proved my Inner Critic to be wrong!*

"That was powerful," I confess, recognizing my outlook on that conversation had shifted by doing that one exercise.

"Yes, it's an amazing tool," Sonia says. "Remember, *mental models drive your behavior.* This is why it's important to identify those that get in the way of your feeling confident.

"One of my favorite quotations," she continues, "is from Carl Jung: 'Until you make the unconscious conscious, it will direct your life, and you will call it fate.'" She pauses while I contemplate what this quotation means. Yes, I could see the effect of my mental models on what I had considered to be fate—until now.

Sonia suggests I keep my notebook with me at work so I can capture all the mental models getting in the way of feeling confident throughout the day. That includes keeping track of my Inner Critic. She says to do this *before* having any conversations I think might be difficult.

> 'Until you make the unconscious conscious, it will direct your life, and you will call it fate.'
> —CARL JUNG

Although skepticism still taints my excitement about this first assignment, I decide to have fun with it.

"I will call my Inner Critic 'Ida,'" I declare. "This is in honor of my Great Aunt Ida who was raised in the Depression. Every time we visited her, she'd share all the worries about the nursing home she lived in, the price of her favorite tea, and anything else that kept her awake at night."

Despite the levity of naming my Inner Critic, though, I still doubt the wisdom of acknowledging her throughout my day. I wonder, "If I'm looking for negative thoughts, wouldn't doing this just invite more of them?"

Little did I know the power this assignment would have on the rest of my life.

CHAPTER 13

Breathe in. Two. Three. Four. Five.

Breathe out. Two. Three. Four. Five.

Breathe in. Two. Three. Four. Five.

Breathe out. Two. Three. Four. Five.

After my third round of breathing, my computer pings a five-minute calendar reminder. It's almost time for the project meeting with Amanda and Theo.

I open my eyes and stare at the blank page of my notebook. Writing in the journal has begun to feel routine. I start looking forward to the release of negative mental models as they flow from the recesses of my brain, reach through my pen, and spill onto the paper with greater ease each time.

Focusing on the meeting, I close my eyes and listen to the stories I'm telling myself about the meeting, with Ida's voice replaced with my own. Quickly steeling my courage, I grab my pen and notebook. The page fills with the stories and assumptions that had been stopping me from speaking up in previous meetings.

They will think I am stupid.

I don't know what I am talking about.

It is not my area.

Theo will think I am bossy.

I am not contributing anything worthwhile.

They already know this.

I will step on Amanda's toes.

I don't have experience in this area.

Theo will be mad that I am criticizing his team.

As Sonia instructed, I go through each mental model and cross out the ones that weren't 100 percent true. Three in particular make me pause.

The first mental model, "They will think I am stupid," is especially hard for me to assign certainty to. *Am I absolutely sure if I say something incorrect, people will think I am stupid?* I look at the statement and think about it a different way. I imagine a friend telling me she was thinking this about herself. What I would say to her? I'd say that if she says something incorrect, it would mean she's misinformed, not stupid.

I decide to be as kind to myself as I would to my friend.

The second mental model, "I don't know what I am talking about," also requires a different way of thinking. I may not be the subject matter expert in a particular area, but I have a lot of experience in different departments. I've worked here for nine years, and I have a strong knowledge of the company's history and operations. I can understand the effect on other departments, a perspective that others may not have considered.

"It is not my job" is the third mental model I reexamine. My job, in its purest form, is about running my team. My job description and what I've been hired to do has changed a lot.

Without realizing it, my role has morphed from the original job description. Isn't this project team just another deviation? My job *has* centered solely on my team and my department, but this project *is* about the company. I realize the scope of my position has expanded, a big part of which is due to this project. I'm not only the manager of my team; I'm now a leader in the company.

Time to leave.

I walk quickly down the hall, taking the last chair as Amanda begins the meeting. I think, "With my mental models exorcised from my brain, Ida's appearance will be limited to brief cameos." I find myself participating in the discussion, even the portions that don't pertain to my department.

As the meeting draws to a close, Theo leans over to me and whispers, "You made several great points today. I don't know what has gotten into you but keep it up!"

I smile at him, feeling my confidence doing victory laps in my head.

CHAPTER 14

The spring sun warms my light sweater, my shadow retreating as I turn the corner. I stroll down the tree-lined street, enjoying the reprieve from the artificial coldness of my office. Today, I'm doing the fifteen-minute walk to my meeting with Sonia instead of driving.

I arrive there and step aside as the coffee house door swings open. A tall man wearing a red golf shirt strides out. I grab the door as it's about to shut. Scanning the shop, I notice Sonia at the back sitting in front of a large bay window and typing on her laptop.

"Can I get you a cup of coffee?" I ask as I approach her.

"No thanks. I've had a lot of caffeine already this morning. I'm switching to water for the rest of the day," she answers with a smile and gestures toward the blue water bottle on the table.

Sonia closes her laptop and slides it into her tote. As she looks up, I exclaim proudly, "It worked! I can't believe how well it worked."

"That's great," she replies. Then after a brief pause, she looks at me curiously and asks, "Uh, would you mind if I ask you exactly what worked?"

In my excitement to share my experience, I had jumped right in without explaining what I was talking about. I looked forward to talking to *someone* who understood mental models and knew about Ida. And I hadn't wanted to show anyone else my notebook. When I looked at what I had written, it made me sound like an insecure crazy person.

"I mean writing down my mental models," I explain. "It was really hard at first. As a matter of fact, it actually felt like busywork in the beginning." I look at Sonia apologetically. "I remember thinking that I can barely make it to meetings on time, let alone spend five minutes before each one writing down my crazy thoughts.

"But on the third day, I saw a difference. Not only did identifying the mental models get easier, but I also realized most of them weren't true. The thoughts that had seemed so strong and debilitating a few days before suddenly felt weak and silly. After doing this for a few days, I could quickly identify them as not true and brush them off.

"What also worked well was taking a 'friend' approach. If I questioned a mental model as being untrue, I considered what I would tell a friend if she shared this thought with me. That," I report emphatically, "usually did the trick."

Sonia asks if I noticed a pattern in the mental models. "Was there a situation, person, or topic that elicited stronger or more mental models than others?"

I open my notebook and glance through the pages. Quickly a pattern becomes evident, and I explain it to Sonia.

"Most people in my company are really smart. In the meetings with cross-functional departments or with subjects I don't know much about, I notice I have a lot of mental models about *not* contributing anything to the conversations and looking dumb. This also happens if an executive is in the room.

"I also notice that when people are really outspoken, I automatically think they know the answers. Again, I believe they know more than me or at least are better than me. Looking at these mental models in hindsight for these meetings, I realize that's not true. As a matter of fact, by the end of this experiment, I was speaking up a lot. And people were listening—even those who speak loud and fast."

I move my notebook so we could both read the pages. Then for our entire session, we review and discuss the mental models. As we finish, Sonia assures me that my lists weren't much different from other people's she has worked with. When she says this, I feel relief knowing I'm not alone with my insecurities.

Sonia sits back. "A little doubt is important for leaders," she says. "Without it, a person has blinders on and may even be described as narcissistic. The key is to use it as humility and openness to learning, not as insecurity and defensiveness.

> When I am humble,
> I seek answers.
> When I am insecure,
> I try to protect myself.

"Look at it like this," she continues. "Humility is rooted in openness and vulnerability. When you are humble, you're seeking answers. You're looking to learn. When you feel insecure and have no confidence, you're looking to protect yourself. This often makes you push others away and be defensive."

The truth of these words is shifting my reality.

Now my goal is for the mental models to become part of my routine so that my role in meetings changes. No longer is my silence a sign of insecurity. Instead, I remain quiet when listening and learning, and I speak up to ask questions and make comments.

I mark this is the first of many victories with Sonia.

CHAPTER 15

As Sonia and I settle into the rhythm of our next session, she asks, "Remember how I told you that confidence isn't something I can teach?"

"Oh, yes," I reply.

"I'm glad. Now, don't get me wrong. Some behaviors *are* associated with someone being confident. But unless you feel confident on the inside, they usually come across as fake or arrogant."

". . . and arrogance isn't the same as confidence," I finish her thought.

"You got it!" she nods proudly.

Then Sonia instructs me to pull out the Confidence Pyramid.

Pointing to the bottom of the pyramid, Confidence in Myself, she tells me I can do more things to add to this foundation.

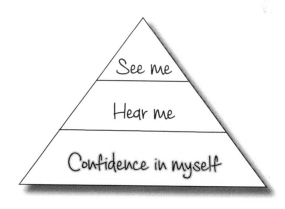

> People who use their strengths are six times more engaged.

"Identifying mental models getting in the way of confidence isn't enough, although it's an important part. Once the models are out of your head, you must replace them with positive thoughts. I'm not a fan of looking in the mirror and saying self-affirmations until you believe them. But I know that when we have low expectations for our performance, we tend to sink down and meet them."

As Sonia explains, we often unknowingly perpetuate our expectations in the feedback we seek. When people ask for input on a project, performance, or just about anything, they often ask negative questions such as "What can I do better?" This is because we often assume the biggest potential for improvement lies in fixing our weaknesses. However, amplifying our strengths is also important.

According to the Gallup Organization, people who use their strengths daily are six times more engaged, while strengths-focused teams are twelve-and-a-half percent more productive. That means instead of only asking about what you did wrong, you want to request positive feedback, too. For example, you'd ask, "What three things worked for you about my presentation?" or "What three things worked well for you in this pitch deck?"

I blanch at this suggestion. "I don't know about that, Sonia. It would feel pretty weird asking for praise."

"Oh! The mental models!" she replies, and I know immediately she's right. *I'm telling myself many stories about asking for positive feedback.*

So, before she could request it, I pull out my notebook and grab a pen to write down my mental models on this.

- People will think I am asking for compliments.
- They won't have anything good to say.
- They will have to make something up.
- I will make them uncomfortable.
- They will think I am insecure.

When I'm done and all these mental models are crossed out, Sonia explains the importance of understanding the positive elements of my performance in the same way I would if the comment were about something I needed to improve.

"Ask for clarification," she insists, "or else you won't know what you're doing well, and you probably won't repeat it."

She asks me to think of a compliment someone gave me recently. I recount to her Theo's praise at the meeting.

"Did you ask him exactly what he noticed? What worked for him?" she asks.

"Well, no," I admit hesitantly.

"What would you have said if he said you were horrible during the meeting? Would you have asked for specifics? And don't just think about this instance; think about other times. When people give us negative feedback, it's natural to delve deeper, to ask for specifics and clarification. But when we get positive feedback, we give a polite thank you and move on. We miss a great opportunity. More often, we make excuses for doing something well and say things such as 'Oh, I was lucky.'"

I immediately recall my recent conversation with Angie at the grocery store. That's precisely what I had done!

For the rest of the week, I concentrate on this approach to growth. I discover that my chance to explore compliments is more plentiful than I had realized. I pay close attention to those who give me compliments. Instead of brushing them off and attributing them to people being nice, I ask questions. People are happy to explain specific things I'm doing well and how it helps or affects them or their team.

What a positive discovery!

CHAPTER 16

The Friday after our latest session, I'm sitting at my desk answering email when I hear a gentle knock on my door. It's Carlos, the IT Director. He leans inside the door frame and I wave him in.

"I just wanted to stop by and tell you your meeting this morning was excellent," he says.

"Thanks," I respond. I'm about to say it's because the attendees were great, but then I recall my last session with Sonia.

Instead, I ask Carlos to sit down. "Do you mind if I ask you what in particular made it good for you?"

He looks at me thoughtfully. "Well," he begins, "you got the agenda out early. I really appreciate that. It gave me time to prepare, and I could tell some of the other folks prepared, too, which made the meeting more productive.

"Also, you did a great job of keeping us on track. That's not easy, especially with Michael in the room." We smile conspiratorially at each other. Michael is known for getting meetings off topic.

"I feel like we really accomplished something," he adds.

I thank Carlos for the feedback and smile. Maybe Sonia knows what she's talking about after all.

CHAPTER 17

I clasp my notebook tightly in my hand as I enter the crowded coffee shop. The proof of my success is evident on these pages, I think.

As I weave my way through a line of people waiting for their drinks to get to the back of the shop, Sonia glances up as I approach. She smiles at me and places a newspaper article in front of me as I sit down.

"Is this your daughter?" she asks. I recognize the picture of Olivia cradling a soccer ball under her right arm. She looks like an all-American girl with her blonde hair in a ponytail and an innocent smile dimpling her lightly freckled cheeks.

"Yes," I respond. "Her team just won the state championship, and they featured *her* in the article. She's excited."

"I bet! That's really great."

I nod in agreement, not bothering to hide my proud smile.

"She was always such a shy kid. She gets that from me. Soccer has really helped her come out of her shell."

"What is *your* symbolic State Championship, Mallory?" she asks me. "What have you accomplished that you're proud of?"

Ten seconds go by while I think about the academic awards I had won in school. But that was long ago, and those awards seem irrelevant now.

Then calmly I answer, "My symbolic State Championship is what's been going on lately. Every time I speak up in a meeting and am assertive with someone, I feel a jolt of triumph. I'm anxious before I speak, but afterward, it feels wonderful.

I won't make the local paper because I gave my opinion on a project, but I sure feel like I had a victory."

Sonia explains, "When you take time to acknowledge and experience your achievements, you build a strong foundation. Each win, no matter how small, helps build your confidence foundation. These successes will provide quick points of reference to use when you feel challenged. They're also good for when you have your performance review. Keep a log of your accomplishments and refer to them when you need a jolt of confidence as you prepare for your next review. They'll also come in handy when you are revising your résumé.

"These victories also affect the wiring in your brain," she continues. "Each small victory builds new receptors in the areas of the brain responsible for reward and motivation. The rise in receptors increases the influence of testosterone, which further increases confidence and eagerness to tackle future challenges. When you have a series of small victories, the boost in your confidence can last for months."

Sonia sips her coffee as I think about this. I understand what she's saying. I know I feel a small sense of victory and a thrill of accomplishment each time I successfully confront Ida. I don't know if Ida will ever be banished completely, but it gets easier each time I challenge her. I wonder what effect it would have to remind myself of my successes and what I'm capable of when I feel uncertain.

Sonia has more to add. "It also helps to remember that others may have done what you are trying to do. Your brain will feel less threatened by knowing what you're attempting is possible."

"Here's that fight or flight response again," I joked. "It seems like my brain is always getting in the way."

"That's right! The trick is to control your brain before the reptilian part takes over."

"The, uh, reptilian part?" I question, thinking I misheard her.

Sonia tells me the reptilian brain is comprised of the oldest part of the brain. This part of the brain contains aspects we share with other animals, including reptiles. It governs our most basic life functions such as hunger and breathing. It's also responsible for our primitive survival instincts, fight or flight response. When survival becomes threatened, this part of the brain takes over, and it can overpower logic and reason.

"The name is not really fair," she comments, sipping her tea. "It's not really a reptile brain. Basal ganglia are found in the brains of early fish, which means the so-called 'reptilian brain' is really a fish brain."

"Reptiles get all the bad press. I almost feel sorry for them," I joke.

My analytical mind appreciates knowing the biological and physiological reasons behind confidence. "But what can I do to make sure my reptilian brain doesn't take over?" I ask Sonia.

"I think you already know part of the answer," she responds. "What's one thing you learned so far that can help you?"

"Mental models. I can check in with myself before the reptilian fish brain gets activated."

"Exactly!" Sonia exclaims, her excitement increasing the volume of her voice.

"One other important thing about feeling confident is knowing what you need from your environment and situation for you to feel confident. For example, if you have a strong need for data or if you know you need all the facts before you speak up, take time to prepare for the meeting. When giving presentations, some people like having a familiar face

> Each win, no matter how small, builds confidence.

in the audience; it makes them feel more comfortable. Other people prefer to not know anyone. They like the safety of being anonymous in case they mess up.

"Whatever you need to solidify the foundation level of the Confidence Pyramid, do it," she says firmly.

We spend the remainder of the session reviewing the critical parts of the Confidence in Myself portion of the pyramid. By the end of the hour, I commit to incorporating all of the elements in my daily work life. I also identify seven things from the previous week I could celebrate.

Walking away from the crowded coffee house that day, I know I stood a little straighter.

CHAPTER 18

My heels click on the scuffed wood floors as I stride across the sparsely occupied coffee shop.

Sonia rises in greeting, shaking my hand affectionately. That is an odd description for a handshake, but there's no other way to explain it. Her handshake doesn't feel like we were conducting business; it feels comfortable and safe.

As we sit down, I place my notebook triumphantly in front of her.

"Go ahead," I motion with my chin. "Turn to the flagged page."

She opens the notebook where the red flag is and grins as she scans the pages following it.

"You've been busy!" she remarks.

"I sure have! Not only have I been doing the mental models, but I have found ten things to celebrate every day." I lean over and point to the top of the page she's viewing. I had numbered the first ten lines. On each line, I had written something I could celebrate that happened that day.

"The best part," I say excitedly, "is that I had my family do this exercise, too. The daily celebrations had such a strong effect on my outlook at work that I made it part of our family dinners every night. It's become our new ritual. Every night, each person would share one thing to celebrate from the day. At first, no one wanted to do it, especially my teenage daughter. But now, everyone enjoys it. It has been a great way to learn more about one another and what's important to us.

"As the days went on, these nightly celebrations made each of us more aware during the day of things we could share. My husband confided to me that it made him more mindful and appreciative during his workday.

"That is wonderful!" Sonia exclaims. "What a great way to share your day and your personal growth. You're showing your kids that even adults have to get rid of habits and learn new things. What we're working on is just as hard as learning a new language. We're rewiring neural pathways in the brain to create new attitudes as well as new thought processes. People call it 'soft skills,' but it *is* tough."

I nod in agreement.

"As you change your behavior, you will feel awkward," Sonia continues. "It will feel strange and unnatural to try something new. Sometimes, when people try something new, they'll stop after a short while, saying it doesn't feel right. They claim that it feels fake. And, in truth, it *is* fake—at least for a time. But then, as the behavior becomes part of who they are, they become natural. When that happens, it's no longer fake."

Sonia emphasizes the importance of this as I try new behaviors. "People work with me to become better leaders. And to a lot of people, a true leader is 'authentic.' But I promise you that when people are learning the skills and techniques that make you want to follow them—these skills you're working on now—they aren't feeling 'authentic.' The experience feels difficult and uncomfortable.

"This is when most people try to quit coaching, she notes.

"When people realize how hard behavior change is, that's when I know who my champions are. The ones who really want to do the work accept the discomfort for what it is: mental growing pains. Others claim they don't feel authentic and use that as an excuse not to try new behaviors or be vulnerable to the failure that might ensue," she adds.

Sonia smiles at me with compassion. Reassuringly, she says, "It's natural to feel fear, worry, and discomfort when you're doing something you've never done before. Remember, courage isn't action in the absence of fear; it's action *in spite of* fear."

"I like that!" I open my notebook and reach for my pen. I open my journal and write, "Courage is action *in spite of* fear."

Although the words sound good, I feel some trepidation. "But what if I try something, and it *never* feels natural? Or even worse, what if I try something and I fail miserably? What if I get the opposite effect of what I want?"

"You will still learn from the experience," she says to reassure me again. "As a matter of fact, you will learn more from failing in life than from succeeding."

I feel myself cringe. I don't like the sound of that. After all, I've worked my entire life to be a success. I do not want to turn into a failure now. And one of the reasons for my lack of confidence is my feeling like an imposter. *Are we going in the wrong direction?*

Sensing my unease, Sonia explains, "Successes are important because they give feedback on what's working. But unless we learn from the small things that didn't work well—our failures and hiccups—we can't have larger successes. It's important to put in safeguards. That way, the failure is small and not very risky. And we allow time for course correction.

"It's similar to raising children. You want them to learn about chores and responsibilities early in their lives. A good parent hopes that they make a mistake when they are young and do things like forget their chores. The child learns that he won't get an allowance because he didn't do the work. This lesson is easier for children to learn when they're young. When they're adults

> Courage isn't action in the absence of fear; its action in spite of fear.

and forget, they get fired from their jobs for not performing."

A picture of my nephew's bedroom flashed my mind. Age 23, he has been living with my sister for the last nine months after losing the latest in a string of jobs. He argued that he was fired because his boss was unfair and didn't like him. My sister refuses to acknowledge the truth about her son: he's immature and can't hold down a job.

"The key thing about embracing small failures," Sonia comments, "is knowing they are opportunities to learn. Looking at the failure as an opportunity to reflect and correct your course will add to your confidence when you do it right the next time."

Sonia sits back in her seat and slowly sips her tea.

"What did you think about the mental model exercise when I first explained it to you?" she asks casually.

"Well, it made sense when you explained it, but it was hard when I tried it on my own. I think I have it down now, though."

"Exactly! And each time you did it, the process came easier, right?" she asks, looking for confirmation.

"Yes," I agree. "Each time was easier."

After a bit, I understand what she's getting at. "Each time was easier," I repeat slowly. "And each time it felt more natural. This was because I could see *how* the stories I was telling myself were changing my behavior and *where* these stories might be wrong."

After making this connection, more insight dawns on me, and I get animated.

"When I did this, and I was honest with myself," I continue, drawing the connection for her, "I was able to replace those bad stories with ones that were more positive—and probably more true. I was able to learn from myself."

I realize in that moment that among the most profound changes from doing the "mental models" activity is understanding how much I get in my own way.

Sonia explains that the mental models of failure are often rooted in shame. "Usually, when we fail, we feel shame for trying in the first place. We feel shame that we're not good enough. This is when failure hurts us. If you can replace the mental model of failing from one of shame to one of learning, you will have a major triumph."

Small failures give an opportunity to reflect and correct course.

She continues, "Mallory, once you embrace each failure and realize it for what it is—an opportunity to learn and look forward—your thoughts of 'I am awful' will be replaced by, 'What can I learn?'"

We spend the rest of our session discussing recent failures, including a performance review that ended with one of my employees leaving unhappy. With each event we analyze, I grow more aware of the power of the mind shift from _critical failure_ to a _compassionate learner_. I see each small failure as an opportunity for learning and growth.

My visceral reaction to the word failure soon dissipates. With relief, I begin to understand that failure isn't a major catastrophe; it only means something had ended with a different result than I'd intended. This would apply to a mistake I'd make on a report as much as a tense conflict with a peer when I lose my cool.

> Replace, 'I am awful' with '
> What can
> I learn?'

By the end of our session, I look forward to seeing what failures I can dissect as I set my pen on the table next to my notebook, a grin spread across my face. "I just figured what I'll celebrate with my family tonight," I announce triumphantly.

CHAPTER 19

Two weeks after that session, I park my car in front of the coffee shop, get out, and hurry to the door. As I enter, the familiar aroma warms me.

Sonia smiles at me as I make my way to our table. I sit down quickly; the excitement of last week's events makes my words come in a rush.

I tell Sonia the unintended consequence of the last session on our family. That evening, I had gone home and shared the discussion on failure during dinner. I admitted to my family that my new mantra would be, "What can I learn?" instead of "This is so unfair and/or awful!"

I continue, "Olivia, my daughter, must have listened closely because when it was her turn to discuss her day, she said it was very challenging. But instead of talking about how unfair her teacher was on the test and how she might fail out of school, she calmly told us about her low grade. At first, I was worried about her almost apathetic response. She answered my concerned look with a conspiratorial smile and asked if I wanted to know what she learned from the 'failure.' When I replied yes, she said, 'I learned that I need to save my TV binge watching for the weekend.'

"'Good idea!' I said to her. I appreciated her honesty and maturity, not to mention the lesson I hope she learned.

"The following night at dinner, she said her day was terrific. She'd asked herself, 'What can I learn?' when her best friend Vanessa sat with someone else at lunch. 'So I sat with Jennifer instead, and I learned we have a lot in common. I also learned

I don't have to feel threatened if Vanessa and I sit apart once in a while.'

"Then Olivia asked if we could make sharing one thing we failed part of our dinner conversation. 'What a great idea!' I responded, then added, 'We also need to say what we're learning from the failure."

I proudly tell Sonia how that one question is affecting each of us. "Now, everyone looks forward to sharing our failures at dinner. Of course, my two children compete for top honors each night," I laugh.

"That's amazing!" Sonia replies. She asks if the failures changed as the days progressed. I replied that, as the week went on, they felt more confident in their ability to learn and grow from their failures.

"What you're witnessing," she says in an animated, grandiose tone, "is the evolution of confidence growing in people. At its core, confidence is knowing you can handle anything that comes your way. This is exactly what you are teaching your children!"

CHAPTER 20

"I think you now understand how important the bottom of the pyramid is. When you feel confident on the inside, you are more likely to try new things and learn and grow from experiences. You're teaching your children to always learn from their experiences, and that failure shouldn't be crippling," Sonia states.

"Before we move on to the next part of the pyramid, I want to show you two postures you can take before an important meeting that will change your hormone levels and make you feel confident. These are known as 'power poses.' Amy Cuddy, a Harvard Business School professor, co-published a study about this, and then she gave a TED talk that has gone viral."

I lean forward, visualizing the two postures as Sonia explains them.

The first one is to sit back in a chair with my feet on a desk and my fingers laced behind my neck. The second is to stand and lean on a desk as I support my weight with my fingertips. According to Cuddy and her colleagues, these poses increase testosterone 20 percent and lower cortisol 18 percent. I recall from my high school anatomy class that testosterone helps us focus and feel powerful and aggressive. Cortisol is the stress hormone that often makes us feel overwhelmed and powerless.

"There have been studies and articles that debunk the effect of these poses. I'm not sure who is right," Sonia says. "But one thing I know about confidence is that your mental state is the most important thing. My advice is if you think these poses help you, then you might as well do it."

I nod, understanding the importance of the placebo effect, even when it comes to confidence.

PART 2
HEAR ME

CHAPTER 21

We sit drinking our coffee in companionable silence for a few minutes. This moment has a feeling of closure, and I sense we're about to transition to another topic.

I'm proven right by Sonia's next statement. "Our brains are wired to trust someone with a weak history of success but who can confidently share ideas over someone with a proven track record but doesn't communicate confidently. Do you agree?"

I nod my answer, thinking about a couple of people who aren't experts but make me feel confident in their decisions and statements.

She asks, "What does someone who is confident sound like?"

"Has a loud, strong voice," I say immediately. As the words leave my mouth, though, I feel a negative rush of emotions. I think of Janette and shake my head. "No, that is not true."

"Those are the people who are loud-talkers, and they are the ones I don't trust or have confidence in," Sonia says.

She acknowledges my immediate reaction and shifting answer. "There is a fine line between speaking *strongly* and speaking *confidently*. It's the difference between pounding your chest out of fear to scare others and pounding your chest because you know you can handle whatever or whomever comes at you.

"Of course, by saying 'you' I mean a gorilla, but people are similar," she laughs.

"When people are insecure it can sometimes come out as aggressiveness as they try to hide it. That old fight or flight response again.

"However, someone who is confident, not arrogant, will leave you feeling inspired and encouraged, not threatened. Arrogance, on the other hand, often makes you feel like the person is out only for himself or herself and usually repels others.

"Soooo," she draws out the word, "back to my original question. What does it sound like when someone speaks confidently?"

I'm silent for a few seconds thinking, then I answer, "To quote what the Supreme Court said about pornography, 'I'll know it when I see it.'"

I continue, "I know what it is *not*: filler words. When people say 'umm' a lot, they don't appear confident." I thought a few more seconds. "As we just talked about, when someone's voice is strong, they sound confident. Unfortunately, I have a triple-whammy here: I say the filler word 'umm' a lot, my voice is pretty soft, and it sometimes shakes. That's true especially if I'm unsure about what I'm saying."

Sonia nods to encourage me, then says, "Yes, there is a lot to the Hear Me part of the Confidence Model. It's not only *what* you say or don't say. It's *how* you say it."

Sonia leans in slightly to signal the importance of this topic. "Let's start with words. Sometimes more is not always better."

In response to my uncertain look, she quietly laughs. "It takes confidence to be comfortable with silence. Let me ask you this: Why do you use filler words? What mental models do you have that make you feel like you have to fill the silence?"

I sit back in my chair to ponder the question. "I've never thought about it before. I think I'm worried that others are judging me, and that they aren't responding because what I said was stupid or unclear—or both."

"That's good," Sonia encourages me. "What else?"

"I'm worried I'll forget an important idea. I talk fast so I won't lose my train of thought. Come to think of it, I also worry there might be an awkward silence, and no one will respond." As I say this, I realize how true this is. Not only do I use filler words, but I also talk extremely fast when I'm nervous.

"Oh, and I also ramble." I say this sentence sheepishly, almost as an afterthought.

"As you can tell, public speaking is not on my fun-things-to-do list," I joke.

"Most people feel the same way," she assures me. "There is a reason that public speaking is often one of the most feared things, even more than death, according to some studies. But silence is a great way to project confidence. Audiences need strategic pauses to retain and understand important points. Also, the ability to be comfortable with silences—whether your own or the audience's—makes you *appear* confident."

Sonia explains that I don't have to have *complete* silence when I speak; I only have to learn how to slow down and pause.

I shift uneasily in my chair. I know I must slow down, but I don't want to speak so slowly that people will think I'm struggling for words. I'm also afraid if I talk too slowly, I will be interrupted by other people who want to talk.

Sonia adds, "One of the most famous speeches in American history is Martin Luther King Jr's *I Have a Dream* speech. Dr. King speaks slowly during the first six to seven minutes of the speech, staying between eighty and ninety words a minute while he gives background information. This is well below the conversational pace of one hundred forty words a minute.

"As he gets further into the speech, however, he increases his rate of speech to build energy and ends at a passionate one-hundred fifty words a minute."

She continues, "He begins the famous 'I have a dream' section at around twelve minutes into the eighteen-minute speech. Then he builds to a crucial point by pausing first and increasing his rate to his maximum tempo. He reaches the climax of the speech—and that climax feels like a mighty chorus of a familiar song, making the audience want to sing with him, 'Free at last! Free at last! Thank God Almighty, we are free at last!'"

"Can you imagine if he'd given the entire speech at one hundred ninety or even one hundred forty words a minute? He changed history with how he spoke that day. While the words of the speech are amazing, I'm not sure it would have made history if the words were read at a faster rate without having the benefit of his vocal interpretation and passion," she explains.

> There is a difference between speaking strongly and speaking confidently.

"His rate of speech and his deep voice gave the words importance because they seem to come from his soul. While we may never sound like Doctor King, breathing deep when we speak helps our oration. It not only helps slow us down but allows us to lower and deepen our voices."

I suddenly remembered something. "I recently read a study that said having a deep voice has definite benefits in business.

Researchers studied the speeches of the male CEOs of almost 800 public companies. They found that the CEOs with the deeper voices managed larger companies, and, thus, made more money."

"I read the same study!" she says enthusiastically. "I'm not sure if it's coincidence or if it can be truly attributed to the deeper voice. But the study shows that a decrease of 25 percent in voice pitch is associated with an increase of $187,000 in annual salary."

She rests into her chair. "The study also showed CEOs with deeper voices usually have longer tenures," she says, then adds apologetically, "I've been told I 'geek out' too much, but I can't help myself. I find all aspects of human behavior fascinating and especially as it relates to leadership."

My smile mirrors hers, and I am eager to hear more.

Seeing my high degree of interest spurred her on. She continues, "I became interested in the effect of voice on behavior during the last presidential election. I was listening to a podcast on the relationship between voice and political success. The speaker said that male politicians with deeper voices have more electoral success."

Sonia goes on to explain a study in which Canadian researchers manipulated archive recordings of former U.S. presidents to raise or lower the original pitch by 20 Hz. (Hertz or Hz refers to 20 cycles per second.) Researchers then asked about 100 volunteers to rate these individuals regarding their leadership potential, integrity, and dominance. In all cases, the participants, both men and women, preferred the leaders with lower-pitched voices.

To make sure the results weren't skewed by the subjects recognizing the voices, a similar study was conducted, this time using candidates. Again, participants overwhelmingly preferred the person with the lower-pitched voices.

Additional research on U.S. presidential elections from 1960 until 2000 found that candidates with lower voice frequencies won the popular vote in all elections.

I shift uncomfortably in my chair. As a woman, biologically my voice is higher pitched than a man's. If these studies are valid, I'm at an extreme disadvantage.

"Why do we naturally give more credibility and control to people with a deeper voice?" I am acutely aware of my lack of tenor as I ask Sonia these questions.

She replies, "I don't think there's a definitive answer. Perhaps it comes down to our evolutionary drive for survival. A lot of challenges during our primitive days were physical, like defending our group against predators. As a species, we evolved to pay attention to cues that help with this. A low-pitched voice sends the message that the person is strong and can, therefore, protect us. The study I referenced found that individuals with low-pitched voice were thought to be more dominant, masculine, and physically formidable. Just like a muscular body, a deeper voice indicates higher levels of testosterone.

"Of course, I can't be one hundred percent certain this is true. I don't really know. Regardless, most of us feel this intuitively. Former British Prime Minister Margaret Thatcher hired a voice coach to help her lower her voice to sound more dominant. Yet, according to voice experts, she lost some credibility because it sounded like she was not genuine."

Sonia pauses and looks at me. "That's the problem with having a low voice pitch," she concludes. "You can't fake it easily."

With a twinge of anxiety, I say, "My voice gets higher pitched when I get nervous. It also sometimes cracks, and my words even sound like squeaks."

Sonia explains that when adrenalin is released due to the fight or flight response, muscles in the larynx tense. "Also, we often forget to breathe properly, and the air will move irregularly thought the larynx, which causes the pitch to change and our voice to crack."

Then this thought occurs to me. "I noticed something with the last few young women we hired: they end their sentences with a question. Now that I think about it, I've heard it with other women as well. I

> Audiences need strategic pauses to retain and understand important points.

don't know why, but it makes them sound unsure. I just heard a keynote speaker at our last conference, and she did this. It was hard to take her seriously."

Sonia notes I had picked up on what's called "uptalk." This is when a sentence ends with a higher pitch, making it sound like a question. So instead of stating "you have fixed all the errors in the report," it sounds like you are asking, "I fixed all the errors in the report, right?"

Sonia says some people do this subconsciously, although it's also a speech pattern seen in some young women in certain parts of the United States. Uptalk is often used by unsure speakers hoping to win over their audience to their message.

"What message does that send to you, Mallory?" she asks.

"It sounds like the speaker is asking for reassurance," I remark about the keynote speaker. "I know she knew what she was talking about. But the way she said things made it hard to take her seriously. Even some of the points from her brilliant book that I'd read before the conference seemed less impactful when she spoke them out loud. I wondered if she was certain about what she was talking about. I felt like she was looking to us for approval."

_____
Uptalk sounds
like a plea for
reassurance.
_____

In my mind, I picture this speaker on the stage and recall an especially painful part of the speech. "Another thing she did was ramble a lot. It made her message hard to follow, and I didn't understand the point she was trying to make."

Being nervous can definitely cause rambling, Sonia agrees. "Nerves may cause you to lose your train of thought, so people keep talking in the hope the train will come back.

"Of course, some people ramble just to hear themselves talk," she says chuckling. "More often, though, they ramble when they start speaking before they decide exactly what they want to say. Regardless, the effect is the same: confusion and loss of credibility.

"My favorite quotation on rambling comes from Albert Einstein: 'If you can't state it simply, you don't understand it well enough.' And he knows a thing or two about understanding things." I grab my notebook and write it down inside the front cover. It's a good reminder.

As I reread the quotation, a small smile creases my lips. A realization comes to me: I have not been rambling as much lately. This, I know, is because I have become more confident in myself.

My grin widens as I share this insight with Sonia.

CHAPTER 22

"What a great observation, Mallory. There are certain things you can do to stop yourself from rambling. Would you like to hear them now, or should we wait for our next session?"

I glance at my watch and realize we only have fifteen minutes left.

"Can you give me one that I can practice, and we can cover the rest in our next session?" I ask.

"Great idea," Sonia responds. "Sometimes I get so excited when people are making progress that I go a little too fast." She looks at me, humility softening her features. "We all have things we are working on, including me."

She pushes back a lock of her blonde hair and asks, "What meeting do you have coming up this week where you want to make sure you are presenting yourself confidently?"

My answer comes quickly. "I have a meeting with my manager and his manager, Robert, to discuss a new process I want to roll out."

Sonia points toward my notebook and instructs me to write down the three key points I want to make during the meeting. I pick up my pen and begin writing. The words come out in a rush, making my handwriting almost illegible.

I look up, proud of the two pages I had written in the short timeframe. "There's no way they can turn down my request," I say, indicating the notebook in front of me. "This idea will really help streamline a complex process."

"Let me ask you this: Have you thought that about an idea before, only to get squashed by a naysayer?" Sonia looks directly at me.

I feel the excitement about what I'd written suddenly flee, and I flinch inwardly. My mind immediately recalls the presentation I gave to the executive leadership team two years before. I describe to Sonia what happened when I pitched an idea about a new line of business. After I gave a detailed presentation to members of the team, they promptly rejected it. A few months later, a colleague in a different department offered the same concept. That time, they supported it.

> Rambling causes confusion and loss of credibility.

"There's definitely something about 'right time, right place,'" Sonia replies empathetically. "But it also has to be presented in a way that others can understand. Communication isn't about you; it's about the other person. If you don't say things in a way others can understand, your message will be lost.

"It's critical to present your thoughts in *their* language and in ways they can understand. This is especially true when presenting new ideas or recommendations. Most people approach presentations and conversations thinking about what they want to say. But who is the conversation really about? Is it about you, Mallory, or the executive leadership team?"

"It's about my great idea, so I guess it is about *me*," I say, knowing it's not the correct answer.

"True, Mallory. It *is* about your great idea. But *you* are already convinced of its merits. To convince *others*, you must make the conversation about them. What do they want to know? What do they need to hear? But I caution you. If you throw all the details at them," she says, "you may overwhelm them.

"For them to see the brilliance of the idea, you must tell your story in an intuitively clear and compelling way, focusing on their needs and their style," she continues.

Sonia instructs me to organize the items into three critical points with no more than three supporting items for each. I do this quickly since my brain automatically categorizes things that way. She explains that these are the key things I need to convey. "Again, only go into more detail if they ask specifically for them or if you ask permission to give more. Remember, the more you talk, the fewer things people will hear."

I nod in agreement. Intellectually, this makes sense. Then I express my concern about my rambling, which I often do when I'm nervous or overly excited about the topic.

She advises, "Mallory, the most important way to stop yourself from rambling is to mentally rehearse, and then keep your points in mind. To do this, before you speak, pause and determine clearly and concisely your point. If you need to, jot it down quickly in your notebook or on a sheet of paper to remind yourself to stay on topic. Whenever you wander, bring yourself back to that main point.

"If all else fails," she says, her eyes glinting mischievously, "dial up your inner Albert Einstein. Do you remember the quotation I shared with you that you wrote down?"

I say in my best German accent, "'If you can't state it simply, you don't understand it well enough.'"

"You got it!" she claps her hands in mock applause.

Sonia suggests I mentally rehearse before any meeting where I'll speak. She directs me to set aside time beforehand

'If you can't state it simply, you don't understand it well enough.'
—ALBERT EINSTEIN

to think about the message and the points I want to get across. I will write these in my notebook, then ask myself how I could get the message across concisely, using as few words as possible.

As Sonia reminds me, "Say what you've planned to say in the way you've planned to say it—and no more. Resist the temptation to explain in detail. Remember, too many details will dilute your message. Instead, sit back and relinquish the floor."

Like the other tools she's given me, at first, doing this may seem hard. "It's because I am not used to it," I tell myself. "But if I plan, anticipate, and visualize being succinct and to the point, I'll have success."

As we schedule our next session, I've already identified three upcoming meetings where I can try out this new technique. I'm excited about this—and even more excited to learn about other methods at our next session.

CHAPTER 23

Two weeks after that session, I'm approaching the coffee shop with diminished zeal. I ease my way toward Sonia, failure dousing my confidence, my feet responding with slow steps.

Sonia cocks her head in greeting, offering a compassionate smile. "It was hard, wasn't it?" she asks.

"It seemed so easy when we talked," I say in acquiescence. "I went in prepared with the outline to four meetings, including the one I told you about with my manager and his manager. I felt good. But when Sally asked me a question about the possible impact of this initiative on Operations, I got flustered. I couldn't help it; I just kept talking. Every time I thought I she was losing interest, I knew I had to convince her how important it was." I pause and gulp for air.

"So, guess what I did?"

Sonia gives me a supportive half-smile.

"Yup, I gave her more information. Thankfully, my manager, Dale, stepped in and summarized what I was trying to say. He was so graceful about it. I felt like a fool, but after the meeting, he said I did well."

I shrug. "I guess we will see during the next budget cycle in two months when I learn if I get money for the initiative or not."

Sonia asks about the rest of the meetings. I tell her they felt more natural, but I still have a long way to go. "When someone asked me a question I wasn't prepared for, or if I had to speak about something I hadn't mentally rehearsed, I'd explain things in too much detail."

Sonia senses my frustration.

"I feel like I'm going backward. I feel like a yo-yo," I continue. "Each time I rambled, my newly improved confidence took a nose-dive. This snag in my progress reinforced my lack of confidence, which made me ramble even more."

At that point, I sit back in the chair, exasperated.

Sonia looks at me kindly. "Do you remember the fight or flight response from our earlier session?"

"Yes," I say. "That's exactly how I felt when I began to ramble. I became scared and talked faster. I couldn't stop talking or make sense."

"Well," she replies, "it's important to remember what's going on with your body and your brain during this time. The best thing you can do is neutralize your biology. By slowing down your blood pressure and having your body—and your brain—return to normal functioning, you'll be able to get a hold of your words and the messages you are sending."

As Sonia says, when I feel like I'm beginning to ramble, I need to stop talking. If I pause for three to five seconds, I'll be able to reframe, refocus, and dim the excitement and nerves that make me talk over people.

Then I look at Sonia curiously. I hadn't yet mentioned my habit of interrupting and talking over people. Once again, I feel like she can read my mind, but I don't push this point.

"What I'd really like to do," she says, "is to make it so you rarely have to use this technique. I want to share frameworks with you that are easy to remember. And effective. Let me introduce the PRES model."

Sonia pulls out a piece of paper and writes PRES, one letter underneath the other. Next to the P she writes *Point* and says, "Begin with the key point you want to make. For example, 'We need to speed up R&D if we want to make our production deadline.'"

Next to R she writes *Reason* and explains that's what is behind your comment or statement. "Keep these points brief and concise. Pick one or two reasons that are most important to the person you speak with. In this case, 'Production begins in three weeks, and we are four weeks behind in testing.'"

I nod in agreement, appreciating the simplicity of the PRES model.

Next to E she writes *Example*. "This step provides an example of why this comment is important. In this case, we'd probably emphasize that by missing our production deadline, we will also not be able to meet our final sales goals."

"Finally," she concludes, "is Summary." She writes *Summary* next to the S on the page, explaining that this step reiterates the main point.

```
Point
Reason
Example
Summary
```

"This is a great process for presenting your point concisely. You'll have a clear beginning," pointing to *Point,* "and middle," pointing to *Reason* and *Example*, "and end that will keep you from getting lost in your words," pointing to *Summary*.

"But you still have to remember the other tricks to stop yourself from rambling, especially during the *Reason* and *Example* steps," she warns.

We spend the next fifteen minutes practicing the PRES technique, first with scenarios she suggests and then with my own. During our final situation, we use PRES to prepare for my next team meeting.

Remember the Power of the Pause.

Sonia offers this one last tip: Slow down. "By slowing down the tempo of your speech, you signal that what you're about to say is important. I call it 'The Power of the Pause.'"

"So, let's give this a try," she instructs. "Write down an important point you want to make during your next staff meeting."

The perfect scenario immediately comes to my mind. I open my notebook and write, 'The implementation of the new software will be difficult in the beginning, but it will create more efficiency.'

She reads the sentence. "That seems like an important message or *Point*. Now, read it aloud. Be sure to pause before and after the most important word or phrase."

I look around uneasily, afraid of sounding as foolish as I feel. "Don't worry," she assures me, "no one is listening." I know she's right; the steady hum of the coffee shop insulates our conversation.

CHAPTER 24

Next, I read the written sentence aloud. "The implementation of the new software will be difficult in the beginning, but it will create more efficiency."

Sonia says, "But I can't tell which words are important. Try it again, Mallory. Pause a little longer before and after the important words."

My eyes dart self-consciously around the coffee shop. I reread the sentence, pausing before and after the words "beginning" and "more."

"Better," she says. "The emphasis your pauses placed on those words really made them stand out. When you slowed your speech, you told me you thought the words were enough to stand on their own. This made me think 'I'd better listen up!' Well done!"

Sonia reaches into her tote and removes a piece of paper with writing on it. She places the paper in front of me as she instructs, "This is a paragraph from a voice coach named Marian Rich. Read this paragraph out loud and pause at each of the forward slashes."

I put the paper in front of me, then I look at her skeptically. Feeling awkward, I read it aloud, faltering on the lines that indicate pauses.

> Mark a paragraph / in this manner / into the shortest possible phrases. / First, / whisper it / with energetic lips, / breathing / at all the breath marks. / Then / speak it / in the same way. / Do this / with a different paragraph / every day. / Keep your hand / on your abdomen / to make sure / it moves out / when you breathe in / and moves in / when you speak.

"It sounds weird. I feel like I'm slow reading this. My cadence doesn't sound natural."

"That's because it's not your natural speech. It's better, at least, to come across as confident and to make people understand what you are trying to say. You are aiming for about one hundred forty words a minute. Remember; most people speak at one-ninety or higher."

I repeat the paragraph five times. Each time, the reading becomes more comfortable and feels more natural.

"Nicely done," Sonia says. "Practice this paragraph every day for the rest of the week. Next week, change the words to your own. Develop your own paragraph. Perhaps it's an important message you have to give or a presentation you need to make."

"Okay," I commit to doing it. I lean back in my chair, contemplating which part of the messaging about the upcoming department reorganization I could use.

"And don't forget to pause. Pauses are good when you want your words to be heard. You can also use pauses to collect yourself when you are nervous or worried about rambling or talking too much. If you feel like any of those are about to happen, take a breath, count to five, and gather your thoughts. This pause is enough to help you reframe, refocus, and dim the excitement that makes you nervous."

I look at my coach dubiously. "I don't want people to think I'm struggling for words," I protest.

"I understand that concern but know that it's a *mental model* you have. Some people will like your slower speech. It's respectful to people who have a more analytical style and who appreciate having more time to process and think. To them, it is respectful to give them this time."

"I can see that," I reply. Then I tell her I feel like that when Justin talks. "He talks so fast, I don't catch half of what he's saying. I leave the meeting sometimes thinking I'm not smart enough because I don't keep up with him."

"Do you want people to feel that way about you when they leave a meeting, or would you rather them feel respected and understand your points?" Sonia asks as she looks purposefully at me.

"And I warned you, the new behaviors are going to feel strange until you get used to them. Especially behaviors that are actually changing the way you do things naturally." Then she reminds me that when I'm changing thought processes and behaviors, I'm also changing the neuropathways in my brain.

"You can help along the behavior change by visualizing the actions. As a matter of fact, many of the situations that pose the greatest difficulty don't come up often. So, you'll have a hard time forming the neural pathways needed to make your new skills habitual unless you learn to visualize them."

I respond, "That's why practicing *and* running through the scenarios in my head is so important." I'm surprised at this revelation.

"That's right," she answers, explaining that our human brain has a difficult time distinguishing between what we see with our eyes and what we visualize in our mind. "In fact, MRI scans of people's brains taken while they are actually watching the sunset are virtually indistinguishable from scans taken when the same people visualize a sunset in their mind. The same brain regions are active in both scenarios.

"Visualization is a great way to practice, even if it's with your mind and not with your muscles. It works well when you are trying new behaviors, whether speaking slowly or shooting a basketball."

Sonia explains how she uses visualization to manage her own emotions, that it's a great way to practice new skills and turn them into strong habits.

"When I'm dealing with a tough problem, especially one that invokes a strong emotional response, I often do a visualization exercise at night. It might sound hokey, but I close my eyes and visualize the situation in which I had a hard time managing myself or my emotions. I then focus on the details of the situation and concentrate on the sights and sounds I would experience if I were there.

"I do this until I actually *feel* those emotions. Then I picture myself acting how I would have wanted to. When I compare it with how I really acted, I can see the difference. This allows me to try both behaviors and see which one works better. And, I'm sad to admit, it's usually the behavior I didn't do."

Driving to my office after our coaching session, I don't heed Sonia's warning to practice visualization in a place without distractions. To be effective, I had to immerse myself in the scenes in my mind. Instead, I'm practicing the visualization technique as I drive, putting my imaginary self in a conversation with Justin about an upcoming deadline.

This imaginary conversation ends abruptly after I almost run a stop sign.

PART 3
SEE ME

CHAPTER 25

Within three days, I have adopted the rhythm of the speech paragraph. Within two days after that, I notice I was combining all the exercises without consciously realizing it: PREZ elements, speech paragraph, and visualization.

Instead of doing each as a separate task—first writing out the PREZ elements of the conversation, then practicing my message using the speech paragraph as a template, and then visualizing the conversation—I am imagining successful discussions with pauses and emphases at the right times.

What am I noticing? *When I used fewer words, people listened more.* As a result, I realize I don't have to repeat my points or answer questions about something I said.

I smile unabashedly as I sit across the table from Sonia during our next coaching session. I hand Sonia a fork so she can share the chocolate croissant I bought in celebration.

I dig into the flaky crust as I relay the most important proof of the last week's success during my coaching session: *People in meetings stopped checking their phones and answering emails when I spoke.*

Sonia claps in celebration. "Your success is even better than you realize. What you're working on is not only *sounding* more confident but also *feeling* more confident."

Then she lowers her voice into a conspiratorial whisper. "You just proved something most people don't know. That is, you can trick yourself into feeling confident. In a way, you were tricking your mind into feeling more confident by slowing down and being more deliberate—and stronger—about what you were saying."

Sonia goes on to describe a strange experiment that examined the relationship between facial expressions and emotions. The researcher had two groups. Those in the first group held a pen with their teeth, making it look—and feel—like they were smiling.

Those in the second group held a pen with their lips. They looked and felt like they had grim faces. Each was given a comic book to read while holding the position. The groups were then asked to rate how funny they thought the comic was. The participants with a pen between their teeth found the comic much more amusing than the ones with a pen stuck between their lips. "The results prove that putting a fake smile on your face is sometimes enough to make you feel cheerful," she concludes. "Similarly, you can trick your brain into feeling confident, too."

> When I used fewer words, people listened more.

Then she shares another study that involved college students. In this study, researchers instructed 71 college students to perform one of two different postures. One posture was to sit up straight and push out their chests, practicing a mock confident position. The other pose was a powerless one—sitting slouched forward and looking at their knees. While holding their assigned posture, the students were asked to list either three positive or negative personal traits they thought would contribute to their future job satisfaction and professional performance.

Sonia's words come fast as she excitedly relays the results of the study. "The study proved what I have experienced working with so many clients—that our posture has a large impact on our feelings of worth and confidence." She notes that when the students were in the upright, confident position, they had an easier time thinking of positive traits about themselves to write down. Inversely, students in the slouched position had an easier time recalling hopeless, helpless, powerless, and negative feelings.

"Many other experiments prove the same thing." Sonia concludes, "Sitting in a collapsed, weak position makes it easier for negative thoughts and memories to surface. And sitting in an upright, powerful position makes it easier to have empowering, positive thoughts, and memories."

I suddenly become conscious of my own posture, and I shift out of my slouching, casual position. Sonia notices my movements and smiles.

I admit that I've always been fascinated with body language. One of my favorite parts about crime shows is when detectives examine a suspect's body language to see if that person is lying. I love how they dissect certain ways the person looks away or shifts in a chair.

"I agree," she responds. "I used to love the TV show *Lie to Me*. But body language isn't only about figuring out what others are thinking. I often use it to check in on myself."

She chuckles at my quizzical look and explains, "When I'm in a particularly difficult coaching situation or just having a difficult conversation, I will mentally check to see what my own body language is. This keeps me honest about my feelings and thoughts."

Sonia then describes a recent situation. "A few weeks ago, during a session, the man I was coaching was explaining his role in an argument with a colleague. He wasn't taking any responsibility for the conflict. Instead, he was blaming everything on the other person.

"Normally, I would have stopped the conversation and asked questions if I thought that the person wasn't being truthful to either me or himself. For some reason, I didn't do that this time. I let him go on and on." She pauses to take a sip of her drink.

"Well, suddenly I noticed my *own* body language! I had leaned back away from the table, and my arms were crossed."

"Oh, I know what that body language means!" I exclaim. All those hours of watching *Law and Order* are finally coming in handy.

Until then, I hadn't thought about using body language to check in on myself. Isn't it only to see if someone's lying or being defensive? However, it makes sense that my body language is sending a message as well.

Laughing appreciatively, Sonia replies, "Wonderful. You will be ahead in our next session when we'll talk more about body language. We can discuss ways you can use it to help you feel and appear confident."

Sonia gives me my assignment for the week—to observe people who appear confident and write down the behaviors and movements that foster this perception.

I walk self-consciously out of the bustling coffee shop, more conscious than ever that every movement tells a story.

CHAPTER 26

Two weeks later, I straighten my skirt as I walk through the coffee shop doors. As I make my way through the crowded aisles, I pause to allow a man holding a cup of coffee in one hand and a toddler's hand in another to pass.

Walking toward Sonia, I imagine a string gently pulling my head and spine toward the ceiling. This mental image makes my back straighter and my head higher. I sense my shoulders roll back and take a breath. I feel elegant and poised.

When Sonia sees me, I extend my hand. She rises from her chair and smiles.

"Hello," she greets me warmly.

"Hi. I'm Mallory. It's nice to meet you," I say, smiling as I lean forward and offer my hand for her to shake.

Playing along, she takes my hand and says, "Hello, Mallory. I am Sonia Russel. It's nice to meet you, too."

We both sit down, and she speaks first. "Well done! I see you took your assignment seriously as always."

"I did," I reply. "I learned a lot!"

"Let's start with the obvious. What did you learn about shaking hands?"

"Well, one of the things is to be the one to initiate the handshake. I've always been passive, relying on the other person to let me know if he or she wants to shake. I also realize that the webbing on our hands needs to meet. Otherwise, the handshake feels incomplete. Looking the person in the eye and smiling throughout the motion is also important. The hardest part for me is maintaining eye contact through the entire introduction. I want to look away or down after the initial hello."

"You did a good job maintaining eye contact with me," she remarks. "There is just one thing I want to add. What did I do differently than you during our handshake?"

I think for a minute and then say, "When you introduced yourself, you said your last name. I only said my first."

"That's right! This is a big difference between most men and women. Men use their first and last names, but women often only use their first. I suggest you own who you are and use *both* of your names!"

I nod in agreement. She's right. I haven't picked up on that difference until she said it. Even at the fundraiser my husband and I went to over the weekend, this happened. In this quasi-business, quasi-social event, I could not recall one woman who used both names in her introduction. Yet for every man I met, I was certain he used both his first and last names.

"Now let me teach *you* something, Sonia," I declare, grinning with pleasure.

I tell her about the origin of the Western handshake I learned in my college cultural anthropology class. I explain that when primitive tribes met under friendly conditions, they held out their arms with their palms exposed to show they didn't have a weapon. During Roman times, people often had concealed daggers, and so the lower arm grasp was developed. In the 19th century, the lower arm grasp morphed into shaking palms to seal transactions. "And that," I say triumphantly, "is how we have come to our current handshake."

"How interesting. I had no idea!"

I continue, "I don't know why I remember that from the class, but I do. It came back to me when I was doing my observations at the busy coffee shop near my office that caters to the business crowd.

Own who you are in an introduction.

"Hold on," I say, reaching for my leather journal in my purse. "I made some notes."

I admit that, in this exercise, my primary goal was to observe people's eye contact. Maintaining eye contact has always been hard for me, and I was hoping I'd discover that eye contact didn't matter. Either that or I'd find tricks to help me. With those people I observed that day, neither of these things happened.

"I've always been a little shy," I confess to Sonia. "I've gotten better after observing those people that day, but it's still hard for me to keep eye contact."

She asks me to recall any specific times when I giving contact is especially difficult. As I think about the question, I realize I was providing the answer. I chuckled at its obviousness.

"As you can see, I don't maintain eye contact when I am thinking. I can keep it when the other person is talking, but when I talk, I always look away to think."

"A lot of people do that," she assures me. "You are limiting the social cues you're taking in and letting your brain focus only on what is going on inside your head. This gives your brain fewer things to process and makes it possible to concentrate on your thoughts."

She pauses to let me process what she just said. "That's why you do it, but what message do you think it sends the other person when you don't look at the person you are speaking to?" As she asks this question, her eyes are darting around.

Ripples of unease replace the connection I had felt before her eyes left mine. The effect was profound! I fight the urge to follow her eyes so I can see what she's looking at.

"Point made," I say.

She continues, "Sustained eye contact initiates an approach reaction in the brain and signals interest in social engagement. If someone averts her eyes, it signals an avoidance response in the other person, and it sends neurological clues that she may be hiding something or is lying.

"Eye contact conveys details about emotions and intentions, providing some of the strongest information during social interaction. Fear is primarily communicated through the eye muscles, but the slightest smile that reaches your eyes, making them crinkle, can neurologically communicate warmth. How you use your eyes is a critical part of developing trust."

Her words bring clarity to what I already know but hadn't yet solidified in my mind. Still, I wonder, "If I've been doing it wrong, what's the right way? How much eye contact should I have?" I ask Sonia and, predictably, she turns the question back to me.

I answer her boomerang question with this: "If I'm comfortable with others and trust them as I do with you, I like a lot of eye contact. It makes me feel you are interested in me and what I'm saying. But if I don't like or trust the person, like Michael, it makes me feel like he's trying to intimidate me. It's almost like he's threatening me, and I get really uncomfortable."

Sonia nods. "A mutual gaze can intensify whatever you are feeling, which can be good or bad. If you like the person, it will add to the comfort and trust. But if you don't like him or her, it can be intimidating and threatening—just as you described.

"In the American business culture, a good rule is to maintain eye contact between 70 to 85 percent of the time. The geographic region and the other person's personality will affect which part of the scale you need to be on."

She pauses to allow me time to consider this point, then says, "Remember, communication isn't about you and what *you* feel comfortable with."

I interrupt her. "Yes, I know communication is about the other person. See, I remember!" Sonia's genuine smile and laugh make me smile in response.

"What other things did you notice about people who seemed confident?" she asks, still smiling.

I again fight the urge to let my eyes wander while thinking about this question. Then I realize I'm not leaning back in my chair like I usually do while I'm thinking. Maintaining eye contact makes me continue to feel connected to Sonia, even as I struggle to search inward for a response to her question.

To help answer it, I take out my leather journal where I had filled three pages with observations and sketches. As I glance through the pages, I identify a common theme.

"Here's what I noticed—that the people I'd describe as confident used hand gestures positively. But for other people, their gestures were distracting and made them seem nervous. One woman kept touching her hair and adjusting her clothes. She didn't seem comfortable; she looked anxious. One man kept twirling and tapping his pen. I don't know how the person he was talking to didn't get irritated.

"Other people seemed to look more natural with their gestures. The way they moved their hands was like an extension of their words, not a detractor of their meaning. I could tell when people were excited about their topics and when they were knowledgeable. Their movements provided quite a contrast to others who fidgeted with their clothing or sat rigid in their seats."

Sonia leans forward almost imperceptibly. Her entry into my personal space adds a sense of intimacy to her words.

"Do you remember the communication percentages I shared earlier with you?" she asks. At my nod, she reiterates a key point. "The body language that accompanies your message is even more important than the words coming out of your mouth. When you use a variety of positive gestures, it's easier to convey warmth and energy."

Warmth and energy. I didn't think about confidence in those terms, but these two words describe the type of confidence I want to portray. This probably explains why another thing I noticed about confident people surprised me: *They smile.*

I tell Sonia about this epiphany, remembering she'd said that confidence is about *believing you can handle anything that comes your way.*

I shift my weight in my seat and re-cross my legs.

Looking across the table into Sonia's warm smile, I realize how vital smiling is to show confidence. A genuine smile is full of emotion, displaying composure and often projecting poise. Her smile—like the smiles of many others I respect—make her approachable and enhance the warmth needed for real leadership.

> Eye contact conveys details about emotions and intentions.

"One thing I notice about you, Sonia," I say, "is you always seem to smile at the right moments. You don't do it too much but enough to encourage me and make me feel confident in your ability to help me. I feel not only that you can help me, but I'm able to be vulnerable because I know you want to help."

"That is so nice of you to say. I *am* interested in you," she says, emphasizing the word "am." "And I'm glad you can see it. Facial expressions of kindness, compassion, and interest cannot be faked. If you pretend you care, the person will pick up on it. And this will do more harm to your relationship than if you just looked at that person with a blank expression."

She leans close, and whispers, "Would you like to know a secret? Would you like to know how you can make people feel like that when you meet them?"

"Heck, yeah!" I say, almost shouting in excitement.

She sits back, raising her voice to an average volume. "Good! That will give you something to look forward to because our time is up now." She laughs as I groan again in mock frustration.

Although I'm eager to hear Sonia's secret, I have enough to work on until next time.

CHAPTER 27

Three days after my coaching session, Dale knocks softly on my door.

"Come in," I say, looking up from my computer monitor.

As soon as he enters, I know he's about to tell me something I didn't want to hear.

"Uh-oh. What is it?" I ask apprehensively. "What's the bad news?"

"I don't know what you are talking about," he says in mock indignation. "I have great news! I was able to get an extra seat for the company box for tomorrow night's basketball game. And it's your lucky day," he says with a flourish, "because I can't go!"

He responds to the look of horror on my face by saying, "Don't thank me now. You can do that after the game. Enjoy!" He leaves, shutting the door quickly behind him to block out my protests.

A good basketball game is one of the few things that would make me endure an evening of schmoozing. While most people fear death and public speaking, I fear making a fool of myself in front of our company's executives. But our team is one game away from making the playoffs, and this could be it!

At the game, I'm sporting my fan gear as I walk into our company's suite at the stadium.

I open the suite door to the smell of roast beef and grilled asparagus. I spot the buffet table loaded with food not found at the concession stand. Across the room, an additional table is filled with traditional stadium food, and I immediately make

RISE: Finding Your Executive Voice

my way to the hot dog station. "It wouldn't feel like a real basketball game without mustard spilling on my jersey," I think.

As I'm putting sauerkraut on my hot dog (something that only tastes good at basketball games), the man next to me turns and smiles. My heart skips a beat as I recognize our CEO, Ethan Perez.

> Gestures convey warmth and energy.

"Hi, I'm Ethan Perez," he says as though I didn't see his photography every time I walk into the office lobby. Plus, I have met him before a couple of times. I apparently haven't made an impression in the past.

"Hi," I respond. My mind immediately goes to my last session with Sonia. "Here's to nothing." I put down my hot dog, hold out my hand, and say, "I'm Mallory Jenkins. It's nice to meet you. Thank you for letting me join you."

He chuckles softly. "Well, I had nothing to do with it, but I'm glad you are here."

We finish dressing our hot dogs and sit down in the front seats of the box. A server approaches and hands us drinks. Ethan and I watch in companionable silence until the end of the quarter, only occasionally talking about the basketball season and my role in the company.

When the quarter ends, Ethan says, "Mallory, I have some people I'd like you to meet. Come with me." I follow him into a throng of people standing behind the seats. The rest of the evening, I feel like Cinderella. Ethan introduces me to so many executives whose names I know but have never met. Each time I say hello to someone, I practice the techniques Sonia and I worked on. I feel my confidence grow with each person I meet.

119

Maintaining eye contact is becoming more comfortable each time.

Once I feel the awkwardness ease, I lose myself in the conversations.

In fact, I'm so engrossed in the them, I miss the entire second half of the game. That's okay because another kind of victory is at hand. I feel accepted as an equal, sharing my thoughts and ideas with people whose titles have always intimidated me.

CHAPTER 28

Monday morning, I'm scrolling through my emails and eating my 10:00 am yogurt, a habit since my first week on the job. My door erupts open, and Dale strides in, a delighted smile on his face.

"I didn't know you were such a charmer!" he says.

Noticing my puzzled expression, he adds, "I just got a call from Ethan. He said he was impressed with you at the game. He asked me why I have been hiding you for so long. I didn't remind him that he'd met you at least twice before."

"Four times, to be exact," I correct him.

"Well, the fifth time is a charm!" he replies. "Whatever you did, keep doing it! I'm proud of you, Mallory. I know you didn't want to go, but you deserve to have some of the spotlight. You're a hard worker and a good manager. You have brilliant ideas. You just need the right audience—and the voice—to show it."

The acceptance I felt from others at the game and the power of Dale's and Ethan's words cloak me throughout the week. Feeling like I had the support of people I admire, I speak up at meetings, even to show disagreement. This is something I've always shied away from. I had assumed that if I disagreed, I must be missing something. So if I were sincerely opposed to something, I'd discuss it with the person after the meeting. I didn't want to make anyone look or feel bad in front of others.

At least that's what I had told myself.

Thinking about this, I wonder, "Why wasn't I worried about hurting someone's feelings now?" In a shocking revelation, I admit that my previous refusal to disagree was less about making someone look bad than it was about me not having the confidence to state a contrary opinion.

This epiphany hit me hard. *Am I that uncaring?* No, I realize, that isn't true. I had used it as an excuse, a view of myself I hid behind. The truth was that I didn't have the confidence to believe my opinion was as important as someone else's. I also thought others must know something I didn't. I simply didn't want to look stupid.

CHAPTER 29

At our next session, I share my revelation with Sonia and what led up to it. I'm able to relay the events of the night of the basketball game with a detached manner. I feel like an observer, describing someone else.

We dissect my actions and words, comparing them to what we discussed in our previous sessions. I'm amazed at how many of the techniques I used, and how quickly they'd become part of my way of communicating.

"Why do you think you made an impression on Ethan and the others?" Sonia asks rhetorically. "It wasn't just that you did all the things to make you look confident. Without warmth and caring, those behaviors would come across as arrogant. But you had enough confidence in yourself that you didn't need to prove you deserved to be there. If my hunch is correct, you didn't feel like you had to show how smart you are about basketball or how much you know about the company."

She's right. The more confident and comfortable I felt that evening, the more questions I asked. I even told a couple of jokes about the opposing team that received laughs. I realize that, although the behaviors are similar, one difference between arrogance and confidence is warmth and caring about others. People who are arrogant focus on themselves. People who are confident concentrate on others, knowing that others' needs and successes won't make them look bad.

"I guess you're ready for my secret now," Sonia says, referring to the teaser she left me with at the last session. "As a matter of fact, you have done so well, I think you are ready for two!"

I nod expectantly—like a little kid waiting for a cookie.

"Both of these are ways to improve trust and increase your warmth factor, an essential part of confidence," she begins. "First, early in the conversation or when you're about to meet someone, tap into a memory of someone you love and respect. This will soften the muscles around your eyes and unconsciously produce a half-smile. When others see this expression, it will stimulate a feeling of trust in their brains. The recollection of pleasant memories will also release pleasure chemicals throughout your body and brain, making you relax more.

"The best part is that they'll unconsciously mirror your facial muscles, and their brains will release similar chemicals in response."

"And," quoting from one of our earlier coaching sessions, I say, "Like you said earlier, Sonia, 'people remember how you make them feel, not what you say.'"

"That's right," she responds. "And here's one more technique to ensure someone feels a connection with you. When you meet new people, notice the color of their eyes. You don't have to remember the color; simply notice it."

I look at her skeptically. "What will that do, Sonia?"

"Try it and find out," she responds. I should have known she wouldn't tell me the answer.

"But for this session, let's continue to discuss your observations about confident body language."

With that, I pull out my black leather journal with my written observations.

I start by explaining I was surprised at how people folding their arms in front of them was different for different people. People who crossed both arms in front of them looked angry, disengaged, or upset if they were also leaning back in their chair away from the other person.

When people are standing in line for their coffee, they often look insecure, not defensive. I look at the drawings in my note-book and notice the difference in these people. The women in my pictures and my descriptions cross only one arm in front of their chests, or they hold a purse or object in front of them. It almost seems like a half-hug.

Sonia calls this is an adult version of a hug. "When we were kids, we were often hugged during stressful times. As adults, women sometimes recreate being hugged by doing a partial arm-cross."

I now realize why I often stand in that position.

"Do me a favor," Sonia says. "Stand up and do the half-hug." I glance around nervously. "Here?" I ask.

"Yes, it's okay," she assures me.

I stand up cautiously, automatically doing the half-hug in my discomfort.

"What do you notice about your shoulders?" she asks.

I look down and to the side, noticing they're folded inward. "If space is body language, does this make you take up more or less space?" she asks.

"Less. It makes me look—and feel—smaller," I acknowledge.

"What else do you notice about your body?" she asks.

I mentally scan the position of my lower body. I realize I'm leaning, placing my weight on my left foot. Then I become more aware of other parts of my body. I notice I begin to rock slightly, swaying gently on my unevenly distributed weight.

Sonia motions for me to sit down. "This isn't something for only women. Men show their insecurity differently. Instead of imitating a hug, men will sometimes recreate the feeling of someone holding their hand." Standing up, she clasps her hands in front of her. "It's called the Fig Leaf." She grins playfully.

I laugh, recognizing the posture as one I've seen in Biblical pictures.

Then I grumble, "Now I'm even more self-conscious! This will make me be even more insecure and do it even more" I feel sure this knowledge will make me so uncomfortable that I'll project *less* confidence.

"No, you won't! I will show you a great habit that will help you look more confident when you are standing. And this posture will trick your brain into feeling confident."

Sonia then motions for me to stand next to her. She instructs me to stand at ease with both feet on the ground, hip- or shoulder-width apart. This distributes my weight evenly, making rocking impossible.

"Now imagine you are a great oak tree with roots firmly anchored in the ground. This will prevent you from rocking, swaying, and moving around. Here, hold this," she says, handing me a pen.

As I hold the pen, I notice my thumb knuckle automatically points forward. Sonia tells me to practice *this position* whenever I stand. "But don't twirl the pen or click it," she warns. "Fidgeting connotes nervousness, which is the opposite of confidence!"

Holding this position, I close my eyes and take in the sounds of the coffee shop. I feel rooted in its center, allowing the chattering voices, the clinking ceramic cups, and the pouring of coffee to whirl around me.

I feel stable and strong.

CHAPTER 30

During the week, I notice how the powerful feeling remained with me each time I practiced the stance Sonia taught me. Each time I become conscious of doing the half-hug, I replace any shakiness with the oak tree stance.

The following Wednesday, I hear a familiar gruff voice call to me as I walk to my staff meeting. "Hold on a minute, Mallory." I feel a knot at the bottom of my stomach. It's Michael, the senior manager assigned to my project that was being delayed.

Michael strides down the hall and lodges himself in my walking path. He stands firmly in front of me, his body erect. "I just heard your team is holding us up again!" His voice challenges me to disagree with him.

That's when I feel my body begin to close into the half-hug. I force my feet into the oak stance and place my hands by my side.

"That's not what's happening. I'm on my way to a meeting, but I will come to your office at two o'clock this afternoon to talk about this," I say in a firm, calm voice.

"I need to talk about it now," he states, anger clipping his words.

I mentally scan my body to make sure I'm standing in the confident manner Sonia and I discussed. I say my next sentence slowly and assuredly, looking into his eyes and noticing their hazel brown color. "I'm sorry, but it will have to wait until after my next meeting. I will see you at two," I say as I swiftly step around him.

As I walk away, I feel a smile spreading across my face. Michael is known as a bully, and I have always avoided him. Today, I'm amazed to realize I don't feel trepidation as I think about our imminent discussion. I know my team members are working hard, and I won't let him badmouth them—a tactic I'm sure he will attempt.

> Warmth and caring are important for confidence.

Within two steps, my smile fades. Looking to my right, I notice my audience—members of my staff staring at me, mouths agape. They're standing behind a glass wall that allowed them to witness the exchange.

"Holy crap," Sheri says as I enter the office area. "Who *are* you?!"

"I don't know what just happened," Daniel says, "but seeing Michael's face as you walked away was priceless. I don't think I've ever seen you stand up to him before. I'm told he's on the warpath about that project delay. Great job, Mallory!"

"Thank you," I reply, trying to hide my self-satisfaction. I sit down and arrange the papers in front of me. "Now, let's get this meeting going."

CHAPTER 31

"It was like I was possessed," I tell Sonia at our next session. "I wasn't even thinking at the moment; I just felt that holding my ground about meeting later was the right thing to do. I can't believe I even told him what was convenient for me! Normally, I would have apologized profusely and asked him what time he'd like to meet."

I catch myself in this falsehood, "No, on second thought, I would have rescheduled my staff meeting and spoken with him immediately instead of making him wait," I admit.

I realize I've had a lot of victories in the time I've been working with Sonia, my conversation with Michael being my biggest one yet. The confidence I've aspired to own sprang to the surface, and my calm strength changed how Michael and my team view who I am. It's even changed how I view myself.

"I want you to think about how Michael held himself in that moment," Sonia instructs. "What did you notice about the way he stood during the conversation?"

I close my eyes to picture him, then open them to describe the image. "He's only about five-feet-ten, but he always seems bigger than that," I conclude.

She nods and says, "One way to show dominance is to take on extra space and maximize presence inside a physical space. Using physical space this way shows that the person may have dominance within the hierarchy. This is the essence of why it feels threatening if others do this. It taps into a primitive need for resources and survival."

> Space is body language.

Sonia smiles as she adds. "This might work well when you're trying to block someone from sitting next to you on an airplane. But it doesn't work when you're trying to collaborate with others." She pauses. "It also comes in handy when you are dating."

She answers my quizzical look by talking about a dating study. In this study, she explains, researchers created two different profiles for the same person and used the profiles for a speed dating event and a Tinder profile. In one profile, the person had both arms folded with a slight hunch naturally resulting from doing that. In the other profile, the person had a more expansive posture, leaning back with arms outward.

The researchers analyzed this speed dating event and the data from the dating app. In both cases, people were more likely to be picked when they displayed expansive and dominant postures. The authors concluded that nonverbal dominance, shown with expansive body language, increases a person's chances of being selected for a date.

I laugh and jokingly assure Sonia that I don't want to date Michael.

"I didn't think so," she replies. "After all, I'm not that type of coach."

CHAPTER 32

I was saddened when our coaching ended two months later. In the ensuring years, I applied what I learned with Sonia, and I felt myself becoming the leader people turned to and trusted.

Now, looking back years after finishing my work with Sonia, I'm no closer to understanding the term "executive presence." But as I sit working in the office next to Ethan's, I know the importance of ensuring I feel confident in *myself* before I can expect others to have confidence in *me*.

There are still days when Great Aunt Ida comes for a visit. I don't let her stay long, and I always thank her for the gifts of humility and appreciation she leaves on her exit.

REFERENCES

Alicke, M. D., & Govorun, O. 2005. The better-than-average effect. In M. D. Alicke, D. Dunning, & J. Krueger (Eds.), *The self in social judgment* (pp. 85-106). New York: Psychology Press.

Benabou, R., & Tirole, J. 2002. Self-confidence and personal motivation. *Quarterly Journal of Economics*, 117: 871-915.

Burson, K. A., Larrick, R. P., & Klayman, J. 2006. Skilled or unskilled, but still unaware of it: How perceptions of difficulty drive miscalibration in relative comparisons. *Journal of Personality and Social Psychology*, 90: 60-77.

Carney, Cuddy, et al. 2010. Brief Nonverbal Displays Affect Neuroendocrine Levels and Risk Tolerance. *Psychological Science,* vol. 21, 10: pp. 1363-1368, first published September 20, 2010.

Erev, I., Wallsten, T. S., & Budescu, D. V. 1994. Simultaneous over- and underconfidence: The role of error in judgment processes. *Psychological Review*, 101: 519-527.

Fischhoff, B., Slovic, P., & Lichtenstein, S. 1977. Knowing with certainty: The appropriateness of extreme confidence. *Journal of Experimental Psychology: Human Perception and Performance*, 3: 552-564.

Gregory and Gallagher. 2002. Spectral analysis of candidates' nonverbal vocal communication. Social Psychology Quarterly, Vol. 65, No. 3: 298-308.

Kruger, J. 1999. Lake Wobegon be gone! The "below-average effect" and the egocentric nature of comparative ability judgments. *Journal of Personality and Social Psychology*, 77: 221-232.

Mayew et al. 2013. Voice pitch and the labor market success of male chief executive officers. *Evolution and Human Behavior*, 34, 243-248.

McGinn, Kathleen L., and Nicole Tempest. 2010. Heidi Roizen. *Harvard Business School Case* 800-228, January 2000. (Revised April 2010.)

Moore, D. A., & Cain, D. M. 2007. Overconfidence and underconfidence: When and why people underestimate (and overestimate) the competition. *Organizational Behavior & Human Decision Processes*, 103: 197-213

Moore, D. A., & Kim, T. G. 2003. Myopic social prediction and the solo comparison effect. *Journal of Personality and Social Psychology*, 85: 1121-1135. Moore, D. A., & Small, D. A. (2007). Error and bias in comparative judgment: On being both better and worse than we think we are. Journal of Personality and Social Psychology, 92(6), 972-989.

Ohio State University. 2009. Body Posture Affects Confidence in Your Own Thoughts, Study Finds. *ScienceDaily,* 5 October 2009.

Gregory, Stanford W., and Timothy J. Gallagher. "Spectral Analysis of Candidates' Nonverbal Vocal Communication: Predicting U.S. Presidential Election Outcomes." *Social*

Psychology Quarterly, vol. 65, no. 3, 2002, pp. 298–308. *JSTOR*, JSTOR, www.jstor.org/stable/3090125.

Strack, F., Martin, L. L., & Stepper, S. 1988. Inhibiting and Facilitating Conditions of the Human Smile: A Nonobstrusive Test of the Facial Feedback Hypothesis. *Journal of Personality and Social Psychology,* 54 (5), 768-777.

Tigue et al. 2011. Voice pitch influences voting behavior. *Evolution and Human Behavior.* 33. 210–216. 10.1016/j. evolhumbehav.2011.09.004.

Vacharkulksemsuk, T., Reit, E., Khambatta, P., Eastwick, P.W., Finkel, E.J. 2016. Dominant, open nonverbal displays are attractive at zero-acquaintance. *Proceedings of the National Academy of Sciences* 113 (15), 4009-4014.

Van den Steen, E. 2004. Rational overoptimism (and other biases). *American Economic Review,* 94:1141-1151. Weinstein, N. D. 1980. Unrealistic optimism about future life events. *Journal of Personality and Social Psychology,* 39: 806-820.

LETTER TO THE READER

Dear Reader,

I hope you enjoyed *Rise*. Building a relationship with my readers and clients is the best thing about the work I do. If you enjoyed *Rise*, help other people find this book by writing a review on Amazon, BookBub, Good Reads, or wherever you think people who love books will see it. If you would like to receive real-life leadership tips, sign up for my newsletter or visit my website at www.ImpactLeadershipSolutions.com .

Enjoy your journey!
Anna

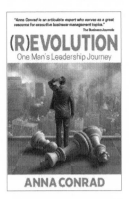

ABOUT THE AUTHOR

Anna Conrad, JD, is the founder of Impact Leadership Solutions. She is a well-known speaker, executive coach, and consultant. Anna has been a sought after expert on over 300 radio programs throughout the United States, and she has been featured in many major publications, including *Fast Company, Inc.*, the *Chicago Tribune*, and over 30 *Business Journals*.

Anna has helped thousands of people reach their leadership potential using practical tips, compassion, and a good sense of humor. A frequent speaker at industry and trade conferences, Anna's high-energy and impactful presentations inspire and educate managers and executives on the behaviors, beliefs, attributes, and skills needed to be successful in today's competitive business world. Additionally, Anna serves as a coach and confident to some of the world's most successful business leaders. Anna is also the author of *(R)evolution: One Man's Leadership Journey*.

To book Anna as a speaker, or to learn about executive
coaching or her leadership programs,
visit www.ImpactLeadershipSolutions.com.

64169078R00087

Made in the USA
Middletown, DE
28 August 2019